Longman Practice Exam Papers

A-level Pure Mathematics and Mechanics

Cyril Moss
Michael Kenwood

Series editors:

Geoff Black and Stuart Wall

Titles available for A-Level

Biology

Business Studies

Chemistry

Physics

Psychology

Pure Mathematics and Mechanics

Pure Mathematics and Statistics

Addison Wesley Longman Limited
Edinburgh Gate, Harlow
Essex CM20 2JE, England
and Associated Companies throughout the World

First published 1999

ISBN 0-582-36924-X

British Library Cataloguing in Publication Data
A catalogue record for this book is available from the British Library

Set in Times 11/13 and Gill Sans by 38

Printed in Singapore through Addison Wesley Longman China Ltd, Hong Kong

Contents

How to use this book

In this collection of eight practice exam papers we have covered the work required for the Advanced Level and Advanced Supplementary Level in Mathematics. There are four practice papers containing questions on Pure Mathematics and four containing questions on Mechanics. The syllabuses for different examination boards vary slightly in content and emphasis, so in these practice exam papers you may find the occasional question on a topic you have not met. You should check with your teachers and colleagues whether such a topic is part of your syllabus or not. Any question on a topic which is not included in your syllabus should be omitted when you work the practice paper, but this should not happen very often.

We have not tried to copy the pattern of the examination papers set by any one examination board. The practice papers here are all of two hours' duration, with no choice of questions. These practice papers are equally suitable for you whether you are taking a modular course or a linear course. Do not worry if you find that you need further time to complete a paper – as you practise each day, you will find that your rate will improve quite dramatically, as will your confidence. The solutions to the questions are given at the end of the practice papers. We have provided you with full solutions and an indication of how marks are earned as you build up the solution. Use the solutions positively, but always try to complete the whole paper first. These solutions are intended to help you to reach your full potential by the time you sit the examination. The mark schemes are included so that you can appreciate how marks are awarded. The three main types of marks used by examiners are as follows.

- **Method marks (M)** are awarded when you know a relevant method and use it.

- **Accuracy marks (A)** are dependent on the relevant method mark(s) being scored before accuracy marks are awarded. Accuracy marks are awarded for correct answers and also for correct answers being given despite an earlier error.

- **Independent marks (B)** are awarded for isolated correct answers or correct statements, and are not dependent on any method marks.

Many students tend to underachieve in the first A-level Maths examination paper they sit. To avoid this problem, sit a practice exam paper a few days before the 'real thing' and get rid of the nerves and inhibitions before the time when it really matters.

Here are a few more tips on good examination practice that we recommend.

- Make sure you have all the equipment you will need: paper on which to write your answers, pencil, pen, rubber, ruler, protractor, calculator (with either new or spare battery).

- Each board gives details in each question of the worth in terms of marks of the whole question and its parts. This gives you a clear message about how much time you should need to solve each question or part-question.

- Most papers start with the shorter questions and build up to the longer, structured ones. Papers are set so that questions are printed in increasing mark order. Experience over many years suggests that the best strategy for tackling papers in which there is no choice of questions is to solve the questions in the order set. However, do NOT spend too much time on any particular question; if you get stuck, leave the question and return to it later if you have time. Never cross anything out until you are sure that you have replaced the work with something better. Let the examiner decide if your work deserves credit or not.

- Wherever possible, use freehand sketch diagrams to supplement your written solutions. Draw accurate graphs only when the question specifically requires you to do so.

- When you have completed a solution always read through the question again to ensure that you have given the final answers as the examiner demands. Many marks are lost by failing to notice this simple requirement.

- Use ALL of the time allotted in the examination, even though you may think you have answered everything well before the end. Use any time left over to check your answers carefully.

- NEVER spend time writing out the actual questions set by the examiner – the examiner knows what they are!

- In longer questions with several parts, you are often asked to show that a result is true in the first part. If you cannot do this do not despair – assume the result is true and write a solution to the rest of the question based on this assumption. This is a common technique used by examiners to give all candidates the same starting point for the later stages of a structured question, when some of them have been unable to complete the first part. Everyone then has the same opportunity to gain all the available marks for the remainder of the question.

- In working solutions, you may get stuck on some particular topic. When this occurs, consult the *Longman A-level Mathematics Study Guide* by the same authors.

Grades

The following guidelines should give you an indication as to how your efforts will affect the grade you receive in your A-level Mathematics exam. Each board has its own methods of grading, but, based on these practice exam papers, you can grade yourself as below and this will give a good indication of the grade you can expect to achieve in the real examination.

Grade A	80 marks and over	**Grade D**	50–59 marks
Grade B	70–79 marks	**Grade E**	40–49 marks
Grade C	60–69 marks	**Grade N**	30–39 marks

Editors' preface

Longman Practice Exam Papers are written by experienced A-level examiners and teachers. They provide you with an ideal opportunity to practice under exam-type conditions before your actual school or college mocks or before the A-level examination itself. As well as becoming familiar with the vital skill of pacing yourself through a whole exam paper, you can check your answers against examiner questions and mark schemes to assess the level you have reached.

Longman Practice Exam Papers can be used alongside *Longman A-level Study Guides* and *Longman Exam Practice Kits* to provide a comprehensive range of home study support as you prepare to take your A-level in each subject covered.

Longman
Examination Board

General Certificate of Education

Pure Mathematics and Mechanics

Paper 1 (Pure Mathematics)

Time: 2 hours

Instructions

- Answer all questions.

- Make sure your method is clear, with sufficient working to show how the answer has been obtained.

Number	Mark
1.	
2.	
3.	
4.	
5.	
6.	
7.	
8.	
9.	
10.	
11.	
12.	
13.	
14.	
Total:	

Information for candidates

- The number of marks is given in brackets at the end of each question or part-question.

- This paper has 14 questions. The maximum mark for this paper is 100.

---

1. Find to the nearest degree all those values of θ on the interval $0 \leqslant \theta \leqslant 360°$ for which

$$\sin^2 \theta = 0.4$$ **(3 marks)**

2. Find the set of values of x for which

$$(x - 2)(2x + 1) \leqslant 3$$ **(4 marks)**

3. The rth term of a sequence is u_r, where $u_r = \tan(90°r - 45°)$, where r is a positive integer.

    (a) Find as numbers the first four terms of the sequence. **(2 marks)**

    (b) Write down the value of $\sum_{r=1}^{n} u_r$ when r is an odd integer. **(1 mark)**

    (c) Describe the behaviour of the terms in this sequence. **(1 mark)**

4. Evaluate $\displaystyle\int_{4}^{16} (x^{1/2} - x^{-3/2})\, dx$. **(5 marks)**

5. In a game, a particular player has three outcomes: she wins with probability 2/5; she loses with probability 1/3; she draws with probability p.

    (a) Write down the value of p. **(1 mark)**

    (b) She plans to play two games tomorrow. Find the probability that she will

      (i) win one game and draw the other,

  (2 marks)

      (ii) get the same outcome in both games. **(2 marks)**

Turn over

1

6. A circle has radius 8.7 cm, measured to the nearest 0.1 cm. Calculate

   (a) the smallest possible circumference of the circle, giving your answer in cm to 2 decimal places, **(2 marks)**

   (b) the greatest possible absolute error in the area of the circle, giving your answer in cm² to 2 decimal places. **(4 marks)**

7. Use the substitution $t = e^x$, or otherwise, to solve the equation

   $$3e^{2x} - 7e^x + 2 = 0$$

   giving the final values of x to 3 decimal places. **(7 marks)**

8. Find an equation of the normal at the point where $x = 4$ to the curve with equation

   $$y = \frac{x^2}{x + 2}$$ **(7 marks)**

9. The points A, B and C have coordinates (1,2,4), (5,3,7) and (3,7,4) respectively, referred to an origin 0. Calculate

   (a) the exact lengths of AB, AC and BC, **(4 marks)**

   (b) the size of angle BAC, giving your answer to 0.1°. **(3 marks)**

10. Two circles, each of radius a, have the centre of each on the circumference of the other, as shown in the diagram opposite. The shaded region R lies inside both circles.

    Find, in terms of a and π,

    (a) the perimeter of R, **(3 marks)**
    (b) the area of R. **(5 marks)**

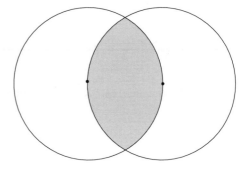

11. (a) Prove that $\dfrac{1 - 5\sin x \cos x + 2\sin^2 x}{\cos^2 x} = 3\tan^2 x - 5\tan x + 1.$ **(3 marks)**

    (b) Solve the equation $3\tan^2 x - 5\tan x + 1 = 0$, finding all values in $(0, 360°)$. **(6 marks)**

12. $f(x) = x^3 - 7x + 4$

    (a) Show that the equation $f(x) = 0$ has a root in the interval $[-3, -2]$. **(3 marks)**

    (b) Use linear interpolation on the interval $[-3, -2]$ to find an approximation to this root giving your answer to 3 decimal places. **(4 marks)**

    (c) The equation $f(x) = 0$ has roots in the interval $(n - 1, n)$, where n is a positive integer. Find the possible values of n. **(3 marks)**

13. The region R is bounded by the curve with equation $y = 4 + \sin 2x$, the lines $x = 0$ and $x = \pi/2$ and the x-axis.

    Use integration to find in terms of π

    (a) the area of R, **(5 marks)**

    (b) the volume generated when R is rotated completely about the x-axis. **(6 marks)**

14. The function f is defined for all real values of x and

$$f'(x) = 3x^2 + px + q$$

where p and q are constants. The curve with equation $y = f(x)$ has stationary points at $(1,0)$ and $(-3,32)$.

(a) Find the values of p and q. **(4 marks)**

(b) Find the set of values of x for which f is decreasing. **(4 marks)**

(c) Show that $f(x)$ can be expressed in the form $(x - \alpha)^2(x - \beta)$ and find the values of α and β. **(4 marks)**

(d) Sketch the curve with equation $y = f(x)$, showing on your sketch the coordinates of the points where the curve meets the axes. **(2 marks)**

Total: 100 marks

Longman Examination Board

General Certificate of Education

Pure Mathematics and Mechanics

Paper 2 (Pure Mathematics)

Time: 2 hours

Instructions

- Answer all questions.

- Make sure your method is clear, with sufficient working to show how the answer has been obtained.

Information for candidates

- The number of marks is given in brackets at the end of each question or part-question.

- This paper has 14 questions. The maximum mark for this paper is 100.

Number	Mark
1.	
2.	
3.	
4.	
5.	
6.	
7.	
8.	
9.	
10.	
11.	
12.	
13.	
14.	
Total:	

---

1. At the beginning of week 1, Rupert invests £100 in the bank on the understanding that he will receive 0.2% compound interest weekly on this investment. At the beginning of week 2, he invests a further £100 and subsequently in every succeeding week with the same interest. At the start of week 3, therefore, just after paying in his £100 he has £$[100 + 100(1.02) + 100(1.02)^2]$ in the bank.

   Find, to the nearest penny, how much this entrepreneur has accumulated on the morning just after he has made his 26th investment. **(3 marks)**

2. A class of 30 students are on an Initiative Test for possible Service Recruitment. The mark for each member is awarded as an integer with maximum mark 10 and minimum mark zero. The table below shows the mark each received.

Mark	0	1	2	3	4	5	6	7	8	9	10
Frequency	0	2	5	2	2	1	2	3	6	2	5

   Determine the median mark, the upper and lower quartiles and hence the interquartile range. **(4 marks)**

3. The function f is defined for real values of x by

   $$f : x \mapsto e^{2x} - 3.$$

   Find the inverse function f^{-1} in a similar form, stating its domain. **(4 marks)**

4. An artesian well of total depth 378 feet is being dug in the desert. On day 1, the first 38 feet is dug and on each day after this a depth of 2 feet less than the previous day is dug until the well is completely dug out. By using an appropriate arithmetic progression, find the number of days required to complete the digging. **(5 marks)**

5. Prove by integration that $\int_1^2 x \ln x \, dx = a \ln 2 - b$, where a and b are exact numbers, which are to be found. **(5 marks)**

6. Find algebraically the coordinates of the points of intersection of the line $y = 3x + 1$ and the circle $x^2 + y^2 = 17$. **(5 marks)**

7. Find the equation of the tangent at the point $(1,-2)$ to the curve whose equation is

$$y^3 + 2x^2(x + 3) = 0.$$ **(6 marks)**

8. (a) Find the first 4 terms in the binomial expansion of $(1 + 2x)^{1/2}$ in ascending powers of x, simplifying each coefficient. **(4 marks)**

   (b) A metal rod of length $100\,\text{cm}$ expands when heated and its approximate length $L\,\text{cm}$ can be found from the formula

   $$L = 100(1 + at + bt^2)$$

   where a and b are constants equal to the x and x^2 coefficients, respectively, in your expansion of $(1 + 2x)^{1/2}$.

   Find the value of L to 3 decimal places, when $t = 0.017$. **(2 marks)**

9. (a) Find an equation of the straight line l_1 with gradient $2/3$ which passes through the point $(-3,2)$. **(2 marks)**

   (b) The line meets the y-axis at the point A.

   Find the equation of the line l_2 which is perpendicular to l_1 and passes through A. **(3 marks)**

   (c) The line l_2 meets the x-axis at the point B.

   Calculate the distance between the points A and B. **(3 marks)**

10. (a) Given that $\tan \theta = 4/3$ and that θ is acute, calculate exact values for $\sin \theta$ and for $\cos \theta$. **(2 marks)**

   (b) By using the identity for $\cos(A + B)$ and the values of $\cos \theta$ and $\sin \theta$, which you have found, show that

   $$3 \cos 2x + 4 \sin 2x = 5 \cos(2x - \theta)$$ **(2 marks)**

   (c) Solve the equation $3 \cos 2x + 4 \sin 2x = -1$ giving all values of x, in radians to 2 decimal places, in the interval $-\pi/2 \leqslant x \leqslant \pi/2$. **(5 marks)**

11. A chord divides a circle into two parts whose areas are in the ratio of $3:1$.

   (a) Prove that the angle θ which the chord subtends at the centre of the circle is given by the equation $f(\theta) = 0$, where $f(\theta) = \theta - \sin \theta - \pi/2$. **(4 marks)**

   (b) Prove that the root p of the equation $f(\theta) = 0$ lies in the interval $[2.2, 2.4]$. **(2 marks)**

   (c) Prove further that $p = 2.31$ is **correct** to 2 decimal places. **(3 marks)**

12. In an experiment concerned with the population growth of a colony of ants, a student believes that x, the number of adult ants in the population at time t days, is given by the relation

$$x = A(B^t)$$

Turn over

where A and B are constants. She has collected these data by observation

t	2	5	10	20	30
x	1430	2460	6130	38 000	235 000

(a) By drawing a suitable graph, verify that her belief is justified. **(6 marks)**

(b) From your graph, estimate values for A and B, giving your estimates to 2 significant figures. **(4 marks)**

13. A closed circular cylinder has a fixed volume of $2000\,\text{cm}^3$.

(a) Taking the base radius of the cylinder to be x cm, show that the external surface area $A\,\text{cm}^2$ of the cylinder is given by

$$A = 2\pi x^2 + \frac{4000}{x}.$$

(4 marks)

(b) As x varies, prove that A is a minimum when $x = 10\pi^{-\frac{1}{3}}$. **(6 marks)**

(c) Find, to 2 decimal places, the minimum value of A. **(2 marks)**

14. A curve is given parametrically by the equations

$$x = t^2, \qquad y = t^3,$$

where the parameter t is positive or zero.

The normal at the point P on the curve where $t = 2$ meets the x-axis at the point Q and O is the origin, as shown in the diagram below.

The shaded region R is bounded by the curve, the normal and the x-axis.

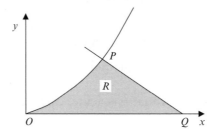

(a) Find, by integration, the area of R. **(9 marks)**

The shaded region is rotated completely about the x-axis to form a solid of revolution S.

(b) Determine, in terms of π, the volume of S. **(5 marks)**

Total: 100 marks

Longman
Examination Board

General Certificate of Education

Pure Mathematics and Mechanics

Paper 3 (Pure Mathematics)

Time: 2 hours

Instructions

■ Answer all questions.

■ Make sure your method is clear, with sufficient working to show how the answer has been obtained.

Information for candidates

■ The number of marks is given in brackets at the end of each question or part-question.

■ This paper has 11 questions. The maximum mark for this paper is 100.

Number	Mark
1.	
2.	
3.	
4.	
5.	
6.	
7.	
8.	
9.	
10.	
11.	
Total:	

---

1. (a) Write down the first four terms in ascending powers of x of the binomial expansion of $(1 - 2x)^6$. **(3 marks)**

   (b) Hence find the expansion in ascending powers of x up to and including the term in x^3 of $(2 + x)(1 - 2x)^6$. **(3 marks)**

2. A geometric progression has fifth term $1/8$ and eighth term $-1/64$.

   (a) Find the common ratio r and the first term a. **(4 marks)**

   (b) Find the sum of the first seven terms. **(2 marks)**

3. $$f(x) = x^3 - 28x - 48$$

   (a) Show that $(x + 2)$ is a factor of $f(x)$ and hence express $f(x)$ as a product of three linear factors. **(3 marks)**

   (b) Express $\dfrac{80}{f(x)}$ in partial fractions. **(3 marks)**

4. (a) Sketch the graph of $y = 2|x - 1|$. **(2 marks)**

   (b) On the same axes, sketch the line $y = 2 - x$. **(1 mark)**

   (c) Find the values of x for which

   (i) $2|x - 1| = 2 - x$, **(2 marks)**

   (ii) $2|x - 1| \geqslant 2 - x$. **(2 marks)**

Turn over

5. The function f is defined for real values of x by

$$f : x \mapsto \ln(x - k), \qquad x > k,$$

where k is a positive constant.

(a) State the range of f. **(1 mark)**

(b) Sketch the curve $y = f(x)$, giving the coordinates of the point where it crosses the x-axis. **(2 marks)**

(c) Find the inverse function f^{-1} in the form $f^{-1} : x \mapsto \ldots$, stating its domain and its range. **(4 marks)**

(d) On the same graph drawn for part (b), sketch the curve $y = f^{-1}(x)$, giving the coordinates of the point where it crosses the y-axis. **(2 marks)**

6. The curve $y = f(x)$ is such that the gradient at any point (x, y), on the curve is given by

$$\frac{dy}{dx} = k(1 - x)(2x + 3)$$

where k is a constant. The point $P\,(-1, -2)$ is on the curve and the gradient at P is -2.

(a) Find the value of k. **(2 marks)**

(b) Find the equation of the curve. **(4 marks)**

(c) Find an equation of the normal at P to the curve. **(3 marks)**

7. The mass m of a radioactive substance at time t is given by the equation $m = A\,e^{-kt}$, where A and k are positive constants.

(a) Given that $m = 0.6A$ when $t = 20$, find the value of k to 3 significant figures. **(3 marks)**

(b) Using your value of k, find, giving answers to 3 significant figures
   (i) the value of t when $m = A/2$, **(3 marks)**

   (ii) the value of $\dfrac{m}{A}$ when $t = 40$. **(3 marks)**

8. The diagram below shows two concentric circles of radii 2 cm and 4 cm with centre O. The points P and Q lie on the larger circle and angle POQ is θ radians, where $0 < \theta < \pi/2$. The shaded region shown has area $A\,\text{cm}^2$.

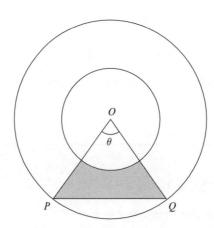

(a) Show that $A = 8\sin\theta - 2\theta$, and given that the area of the shaded region is one fifteenth the area of the circle with radius 4 cm, show that

$$60\sin\theta - 15\theta - 8\pi = 0.$$ **(5 marks)**

(b) Use the Newton–Raphson process once with $\pi/5$ as a first approximation to θ to find a second approximation, giving your answer to 2 decimal places. **(4 marks)**

9. A large delivery firm employs a total of 120 drivers. The distances travelled, in km, in a particular week by the drivers are shown in the table below.

Distance (s km)	$300 \leqslant s < 340$	$340 \leqslant s < 360$	$360 \leqslant s < 390$	$390 \leqslant s < 440$
No. of drivers	30	30	30	30

(a) Construct a histogram to represent this information. **(5 marks)**

(b) Showing all your working clearly, estimate the mean and the standard deviation of the distribution. **(5 marks)**

10. (a) Find the values of x in the interval $0 \leqslant x \leqslant 2\pi$ which satisfy

    (i) $\sin(2x - \pi/3) = 1/2$, **(4 marks)**

    (ii) $\sec^2 x - \tan x - 3 = 0$. **(4 marks)**

(b) Three points A, B and C lie on horizontal ground with A due north of B. The point C lies 200 km from A on a bearing of $065°$ and the distance between B and C is 350 km.

Calculate the bearing of B from C. **(6 marks)**

11. A sketch of the curve $y = (1 + 2x)\,e^{-x}$ is shown below. The curve crosses the axes at A and B. At M on the curve the gradient is zero and the line MN is parallel to the y-axis.

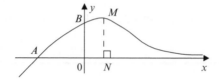

(a) State the coordinates of A and B. **(2 marks)**

(b) Find $\dfrac{dy}{dx}$ and hence show that $\dfrac{d^2y}{dx^2} = (2x - 3)\,e^{-x}$. **(4 marks)**

(c) Find the coordinates of M and prove that the value of y at M is a maximum. **(3 marks)**

(d) Use integration to find the area of the finite region bounded by the curve, the x-axis and the line MN. **(6 marks)**

Total: 100 marks

Longman Examination Board

General Certificate of Education

Pure Mathematics and Mechanics

Paper 4 (Pure Mathematics)

Time: 2 hours

Instructions

■ Answer all questions.

■ Make sure your method is clear, with sufficient working to show how the answer has been obtained.

Information for candidates

■ The number of marks is given in brackets at the end of each question or part-question.

■ This paper has 11 questions. The maximum mark for this paper is 100.

Number	Mark
1.	
2.	
3.	
4.	
5.	
6.	
7.	
8.	
9.	
10.	
11.	
Total:	

---

1. (a) Given that $x = 3 + \sqrt{7}$, find the value of $x + \dfrac{2}{x}$, without using a calculator.

    (2 marks)

    (b) Hence find the value of $x^2 + \dfrac{4}{x^2}$. **(2 marks)**

2. (a) Factorise $1 - 3^{2x}$. **(1 mark)**

    (b) Show that $1 - 3^x$, $1 - 3^{2x}$ and $1 + 3^x - 3^{2x} - 3^{3x}$ are successive terms in a geometric progression. **(2 marks)**

    (c) Find the next term in the progression. **(2 marks)**

3. A particle P describes a curve such that at time t seconds, $t > 0$, P is at the point (x, y) given by

    $$x = 3 \sin t - \sin 3t, \qquad y = 3 \cos t - \cos 3t.$$

    (a) Show that $x^2 + y^2 = 10 - 6 \cos 2t$. **(4 marks)**

    (b) Hence find the smallest value of t when the distance of P from the origin is greatest, and state the distance OP in this case. **(3 marks)**

4. (a) By considering a sketch of the curve $y = \ln x$ and a particular straight line, show that the equation $\ln x + x - 4 = 0$ has only one real root, α. **(2 marks)**

    (b) Show that α lies in the interval $[2.9, 3.0]$. **(2 marks)**

    (c) By using the bisection method, or otherwise, find α correct to 3 decimal places. **(3 marks)**

10

5. The line L has equation $4x - 2y + 11 = 0$.

    (a) Find an equation of the line M which is perpendicular to L and passes through the point $A(3, -1)$. **(3 marks)**

    (b) The point B is the reflection of A in L. Find the coordinates of B. **(5 marks)**

6. The diagram below shows the graph of $y = f(x)$.

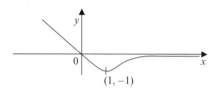

    The curve passes through the origin and has a minimum point at $(1, -1)$. Sketch on separate diagrams the graphs of

    (a) $y = f(x) + 2$, **(3 marks)**

    (b) $y = f(x + 2)$, **(3 marks)**

    (c) $y = f(2x)$, **(3 marks)**

    showing on each sketch the coordinates of the minimum point.

7. A sphere of radius r has surface area A and volume V.

    (a) Show that $V^2 = \dfrac{S^3}{36\pi}$ **(2 marks)**

    (b) Hence show that $\dfrac{dV}{dS} = \dfrac{r}{2}$ **(4 marks)**

    The volume of the sphere is increasing at $4\,\text{cm}^3$ per minute when the volume of the sphere is $36\,\pi\,\text{cm}^3$.

    (c) Find the rate at which the surface area is increasing at this instant. **(4 marks)**

8. (a) Express $\dfrac{1}{(15 - x)(60 - x)}$ in partial fractions. **(2 marks)**

    (b) In a chemical reaction the amount $x\,\text{kg}$ of a substance formed at time t hours after the reaction has started satisfies the equation

    $$\frac{dx}{dt} = k(15 - x)(60 - x)$$

    where k is a constant.

    Given that $6\,\text{kg}$ of the substance is formed after 20 minutes, show that $11.4\,\text{kg}$ of the substance is formed after 1 hour. **(8 marks)**

9. (a) (i) Find the coefficient of x^4 in the expansion of $(1 + x)^{14}$ in ascending powers of x. **(2 marks)**

        (ii) Show that the coefficients of x^4, x^5 and x^6 in this expansion form three successive terms of an arithmetic progression. **(3 marks)**

    (b) The first and second terms of an arithmetic series are 1001 and 2002 respectively and the sum of the first n terms is S_n.

    Find the least value of n for which $S_n > 1\,001\,000$. **(5 marks)**

Turn over

10. A curve C is given parametrically by the equations

$$x = \cos^3 t, \qquad y = \sin^3 t, \qquad 0 < t < \pi/4.$$

(a) Find $\dfrac{dy}{dx}$ in terms of t. **(4 marks)**

(b) Show that the normal to C at $P(\cos^3 t, \sin^3 t)$ has equation

$$x \cos t - y \sin t = \cos^4 t - \sin^4 t.$$ **(3 marks)**

(c) Prove that $\cos^4 t - \sin^4 t = \cos 2t$. **(2 marks)**

The normal at P meets the x-axis at A and the y-axis at B.

(d) Prove that the length of AB is $2 \cot 2t$. **(5 marks)**

11. The diagram below shows the arc of the parabola $x = c - y^2$ cut off by the y-axis at A and B and c is a constant.

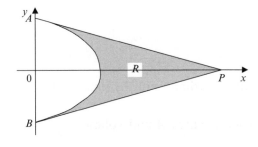

(a) Given that A is the point $(0,3)$ and B is the point $(0,-3)$, show that $c = 9$. **(1 mark)**

The tangents to the parabola at A and B meet at the point P.

The shaded region R is bounded by the tangents and the parabola.

(b) Show that P is the point $(18,0)$. **(5 marks)**

(c) Use integration to find the area of R. **(5 marks)**

The region R is rotated through π radians about the x-axis to form the solid nose cone of a rocket.

(d) Given that the unit of length is the metre, find in m^3, to one decimal place, the volume of the nose cone. **(5 marks)**

Total: 100 marks

Longman Examination Board

General Certificate of Education

Pure Mathematics and Mechanics

Paper 5 (Mechanics)

Time: 2 hours

Instructions

- Answer all questions.

- Make sure your method is clear, with sufficient working to show how the answer has been obtained.

- Wherever possible, draw diagrams to support your answer.

Information for candidates

- The number of marks is given in brackets at the end of each question or part-question.

- Take g to be $9.8\,\text{ms}^{-2}$.

- This paper has 10 questions. The maximum mark for this paper is 100.

Number	Mark
1.	
2.	
3.	
4.	
5.	
6.	
7.	
8.	
9.	
10.	
Total:	

---

1. A high-speed train moving at $60\,\text{ms}^{-1}$ starts to retard uniformly at a point A. The train passes the point B 40 s later and the distance between A and B is 2000 m. The train comes to rest at the point C.

   Find the magnitude of the uniform retardation and the distance between B and C.

   (6 marks)

2. A force $\mathbf{R}$, of magnitude 70 N, acts parallel to the vector $\mathbf{i}$. Given that $\mathbf{R} = \mathbf{P} + \mathbf{Q}$, where $\mathbf{P}$ and $\mathbf{Q}$ are forces parallel to the vectors $4\mathbf{i} + 3\mathbf{j}$ and $-3\mathbf{i} - 4\mathbf{j}$ respectively, calculate the vectors $\mathbf{P}$ and $\mathbf{Q}$ in terms of $\mathbf{i}$ and $\mathbf{j}$. **(7 marks)**

3. A body B, of mass 4 kg, is placed on a rough horizontal table where the coefficient of friction between B and the table is 3/4. A force of magnitude P newtons, acting at an angle α to the horizontal, is applied to B. The magnitude of the normal contact force between B and the plane has magnitude $2g$ newtons and B is on the point of moving.

   Find the values of P and $\tan\alpha$. **(8 marks)**

4. Two uniform small spheres, A and B, of mass 0.1 kg and 0.2 kg respectively, are moving towards each other with speeds of $3\,\text{ms}^{-1}$ and $1\,\text{ms}^{-1}$, respectively. They collide and move away from each other with the same speed $u\,\text{ms}^{-1}$. Find

   (a) the value of u, **(3 marks)**

   (b) the loss in kinetic energy due to the collision, **(3 marks)**

   (c) the impulse exerted by B on A in the collision. **(3 marks)**

   Turn over

13

5. A particle P moves in a straight line so that at time t seconds, $t \geqslant 0$, the acceleration of P is $(2 + 4t)\,\mathrm{ms}^{-2}$. At time $t = 0$, P is at the point O and its speed is $3\,\mathrm{ms}^{-1}$. Find

    (a) the speed of P when $t = 3$, **(5 marks)**

    (b) the distance covered by P between the instants $t = 1$ and $t = 3$. **(5 marks)**

6. Two particles, of mass $0.90\,\mathrm{kg}$ and $0.85\,\mathrm{kg}$, are connected by a light inextensible string, passing over a smooth fixed pulley. When the particles are released from rest, the heavier one moves down with acceleration λg, where λ is a constant. Find

    (a) the value of λ, **(5 marks)**

    (b) the tension in the string, **(2 marks)**

    (c) the change in potential energy of the system in the first 2 seconds of motion. **(4 marks)**

7. An electric car of mass $800\,\mathrm{kg}$ has an engine whose power is constant at $40\,\mathrm{kW}$. The car moves on a straight horizontal road, starting from rest.

    (a) Ignoring all resistive forces, find the time required by the car to reach a speed of $20\,\mathrm{ms}^{-1}$. **(9 marks)**

    (b) Sketch a velocity–time graph for the motion of this car. **(2 marks)**

8. A uniform rectangular lamina $ABCD$ has AB of length $6\,\mathrm{m}$ and BC of length $4\,\mathrm{m}$. A square of edge $2\,\mathrm{m}$ is removed to include the corner D.

    (a) Find the distance of the centre of mass of the remainder from AB, and from BC. **(8 marks)**

    The remainder is now freely suspended from the corner C and hangs in equilibrium.

    (b) Find, to the nearest degree, the acute angle between BC and the vertical. **(4 marks)**

9. A gymnast of mass $70\,\mathrm{kg}$ swings on a rope of length $10\,\mathrm{m}$ which is fixed at its upper end. At the start, the rope is inclined at $70°$ to the downward vertical, the gymnast holds on to the free lower end of the taut rope and she starts from rest.

    (a) Use the energy conservation principle to estimate her speed when the rope is vertical. **(5 marks)**

    (b) Find an estimate for the greatest tension in the rope during her swing. **(5 marks)**

    (c) State two modelling assumptions which you have made about the rope in your estimates and one modelling assumption which you have made about the gymnast. **(3 marks)**

10. A tennis ball is hit on the half-volley at a point A at ground level on a horizontal court with speed $u\,\mathrm{ms}^{-1}$ at an angle of elevation of $33°$. The ball strikes level ground behind the court at the point B, where $AB = 26\,\mathrm{m}$.

    (a) Giving your answers to 3 significant figures, estimate

        (i) the value of u, **(6 marks)**

        (ii) the greatest height attained by the ball above the court, **(3 marks)**

        (iii) the time taken by the ball to reach B from A. **(2 marks)**

    (b) State two modelling assumptions which you have made in arriving at your estimates. **(2 marks)**

Total: 100 marks

Longman
Examination Board

General Certificate of Education

Pure Mathematics and Mechanics

Paper 6 (Mechanics)

Time: 2 hours

Instructions

- Answer all questions.

- Make sure your method is clear, with sufficient working to show how the answer has been obtained.

- Wherever possible, draw diagrams to support your answer.

Information for candidates

- The number of marks is given in brackets at the end of each question or part-question.

- Take g to be $9.8\,\text{ms}^{-2}$.

- This paper has 10 questions. The maximum mark for this paper is 100.

Number	Mark
1.	
2.	
3.	
4.	
5.	
6.	
7.	
8.	
9.	
10.	
Total:	

---

1. The horizontal forces shown in the diagram below act on a particle which is in equilibrium. Calculate the value of P and of α. **(6 marks)**

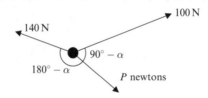

2. A body of mass $9\,M$ is placed on a smooth horizontal bench and is connected by two light inextensible strings to bodies of masses $5\,M$ and $7\,M$ hanging freely over fixed smooth pegs at opposite ends of the bench, as shown in the diagram opposite.

   The system is released from rest with the strings taut. Modelling the bodies as particles, find the acceleration of the body on the bench and the difference in magnitude of the tensions in the strings. **(7 marks)**

3. A car and a motorcycle pass a point A on a dual carriageway at the same instant. The car moves with constant speed $17\,\text{ms}^{-1}$. The motorcycle increases its speed of $10\,\text{ms}^{-1}$ at A with constant acceleration $0.8\,\text{ms}^{-2}$ until it overtakes the car at the point B.

Turn over

(a) Calculate

    (i) the distance AB,   **(4 marks)**

    (ii) the speed of the motorcycle at B.   **(2 marks)**

(b) Draw a speed–time sketch for the motion of each vehicle while moving from A to B.

                                                                        (2 marks)

4. A force of magnitude 1.4 N acts on a particle P, of mass 0.2 kg, for 3 s, causing it to start from rest and move in a horizontal straight line.

(a) Find the speed acquired by P and the distance covered.   **(4 marks)**

A constant retarding force now acts on P and it comes to rest after moving in the line for a further 35 m.

(b) Find the magnitude of this retarding force and the time for which it acts.   **(4 marks)**

5. The uniform rod AB has length 8 m and mass 15 kg. The rod rests in limiting equilibrium at $32°$ to the horizontal with the end A on rough horizontal ground and the end B against a smooth vertical wall. The coefficient of friction between the rod and the ground is μ.

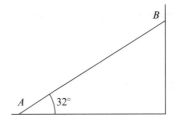

(a) Find the magnitude of the force exerted by the wall on the rod.   **(5 marks)**

(b) Find also the value of μ.   **(4 marks)**

(c) One piece of information given need not necessarily be used in solving this problem. Identify this piece of information and explain why.   **(1 mark)**

6. A projectile is fired with speed $20\,\text{ms}^{-1}$ at $37°$ to the horizontal from a fixed point A on a cliff at a height of 42 m above the sea. The projectile hits the sea at the point B.

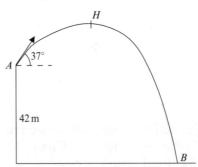

(a) Find the time taken by the projectile to reach its highest point H and the height of H above the sea.   **(5 marks)**

(b) Hence find the time taken by the projectile to reach the sea.   **(4 marks)**

(c) Find the horizontal displacement of B from A.   **(2 marks)**

7. A light elastic string has natural length 1.5 m and modulus of elasticity 70 N. A particle P is tied to one end of the string and the other end is attached to a fixed point B.

The particle moves in a horizontal circular path whose centre C is vertically below B with constant speed $v\,\text{ms}^{-1}$. The radius of the circular path is 2 m and the length of the stretched string is 2.5 m. Find

    (a)   the tension in the string,   **(3 marks)**

    (b)   the weight of the particle,   **(4 marks)**

    (c)   the value of v.   **(4 marks)**

8.   The particles X and Y are of mass 0.3 kg and 0.4 kg respectively. The particles are moving in the same line, X with speed 6 ms^{-1} towards Y which is moving with speed 2 ms^{-1} in the same direction. The particles collide and Y exerts an impulse of 1.2 Ns on X in the collision.

    (a)   Find the speed of X after the collision.   **(2 marks)**

    (b)   Find the coefficient of restitution between X and Y.   **(5 marks)**

    (c)   Find the loss in kinetic energy due to the collision.   **(3 marks)**

    (d)   Under what conditions in such a collision between two particles is there no energy loss? State the value of the coefficient of restitution in such a case.   **(2 marks)**

9.   A horizontal platform is moving up and down vertically with simple harmonic motion. The period of the motion is 2.6 seconds and the amplitude of the motion is 2.8 metres.

    (a)   Find the greatest speed and the greatest acceleration of the platform and state precisely when each of these greatest values occur.   **(6 marks)**

    (b)   Find the distance of the platform from the centre of its motion when the speed is 3 ms^{-1}.
                                                                      (3 marks)

   At an instant when the platform is at its lowest position L, a body is placed on the platform. The body leaves the platform at a height of h metres above L.

    (c)   Find the value of h.   **(4 marks)**

10. *The effect of gravitation forces may be neglected in this question.*
    At time t seconds, the only force acting on a small body of mass 2 kg is $(3\mathbf{i} + 12t^2\mathbf{k})$ newtons. When $t = 0$ the velocity of the body is $(4\mathbf{i} - 2\mathbf{j})$ ms^{-1} and the body is at the point with position vector $(\mathbf{i} + \mathbf{j} + \mathbf{k})$, with respect to an origin O.

   Find at the instant when $t = 2$,

    (a)   the momentum of the body,   **(7 marks)**

    (b)   the kinetic energy of the body,   **(2 marks)**

    (c)   the position vector of the body with respect to O.   **(5 marks)**

                                                                      Total: 100 marks

Longman Examination Board

General Certificate of Education

Pure Mathematics and Mechanics

Paper 7 (Mechanics)

Time: 2 hours

Instructions

- Answer all questions.

- Make sure your method is clear, with sufficient working to show how the answer has been obtained.

- Whenever possible, draw diagrams to support your answer.

Information for candidates

- The number of marks is given in brackets at the end of each question or part-question.

- Take g to be $9.8 \, \text{ms}^{-2}$.

- This paper has 10 questions. The maximum mark for this paper is 100.

Number	Mark
1.	
2.	
3.	
4.	
5.	
6.	
7.	
8.	
9.	
10.	
Total:	

---

1. A particle P of mass m, moving along the positive x-axis towards the origin O is subject to a single force of magnitude mcx^2, where c is a positive constant, acting towards O.

   Given that P starts from rest when $x = a$, find the speed of P when it reaches O, giving your answer in terms of a and c. **(6 marks)**

2. The diagram opposite shows a particle A of mass $10\,m$ on a smooth plane inclined at $\arcsin 0.6$ to the horizontal. A light inextensible string has one end tied to A; it passes over a smooth pulley at the top of the plane and has a particle B of mass $8\,m$ tied at the other end. The particles are released from rest with the string taut.

   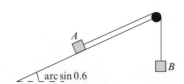

   Find

   (a) the acceleration of A in terms of g, **(5 marks)**

   (b) the tension in the string in terms of m and g. **(2 marks)**

3. A particle of mass m is tied to one end of a light elastic string whose natural length is L and whose modulus of elasticity is $12mg$. The other end of the string is tied to a fixed point A on a smooth horizontal bench. The particle is held at rest at a point B on the bench at a distance $3L/2$ from A and released from rest.

By using the principle of conservation of mechanical energy, find the speed of the particle when the string first becomes slack, giving your answer in terms of g and L. **(7 marks)**

4. A car of mass 1000 kg describes a horizontal circle of radius 100 m at a constant speed of 21 ms^{-1} on a track which is inclined at an angle α to the horizontal.

   (a) Given that the car has no tendency to side-slip, find the value of α giving your answer to the nearest 0.1°. **(7 marks)**

   (b) Explain briefly how you have modelled the car in your solution and how you could refine the solution further to give greater realism. **(3 marks)**

5. A pump raises water from a depth of 20 m and discharges it horizontally through a pipe, of radius 0.1 m, at a speed of 6 ms^{-1}.

   (a) Calculate the work done by the pump in 1 second. **(6 marks)**

   (b) The water impinges with speed 6 ms^{-1} horizontally on a vertical wall and the water does not rebound. Calculate, in N, to the nearest N, the force exerted by the water on the wall. **(4 marks)**

   Note: In your solution, take the mass of 1 m^3 of water to be 1000 kg.

6. The magnitude of the gravitational force between two spherical bodies centres A and B of masses M and m respectively is

$$\frac{GMm}{R^2}$$

   where $AB = R$ metres and the constant $G = 6.67 \times 10^{-11} \text{m}^3 \text{kg}^{-1} \text{s}^{-2}$. Assuming that the moon is a uniform sphere of radius 1.74×10^6 metres and mass 7.36×10^{22} kg,

   (a) show that the acceleration due to gravity at the moon's surface is approximately 1.62 ms^{-2}, **(4 marks)**

   (b) find the time taken for a rock to fall freely through 100 m from rest near the surface of the moon, **(3 marks)**

   (c) find the weight on the earth's surface of a rock showing a weight of 124 N on the surface of the moon. **(3 marks)**

7. A particle P is projected from a point O with speed 30 ms^{-1} at 40° to the horizontal and P just clears the top of a vertical post whose base is at a horizontal distance of 70 m from O. Find

   (a) the height of the post, **(6 marks)**

   (b) the *velocity* of P at the instant when it just clears the post. **(6 marks)**

8. The diagram opposite shows a uniform rod AB, of length $2l$ and mass M, with the end A resting on rough horizontal ground. The end B is connected by a light string to a point C on the ground and the points A, B and C are in the same vertical plane. The rod AB and the string BC make angles of 60° and 30° with the horizontal respectively when the rod is on the point of slipping.

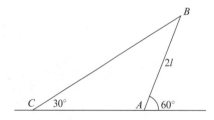

   (a) Find the coefficient of friction between the rod and the ground. **(8 marks)**

   (b) Given that the string is elastic of natural length $l\sqrt{3}$, find the modulus of elasticity of the string in terms of M and g. **(4 marks)**

Turn over

9. A particle P is projected vertically upwards with speed $u\,\mathrm{ms}^{-1}$ from ground level. Between the times $2\,\mathrm{s}$ and $3\,\mathrm{s}$ after leaving the ground, P rises $45\,\mathrm{m}$.

   (a) Find
       (i) the value of u,   **(5 marks)**

       (ii) the greatest height achieved by P,   **(3 marks)**

       (iii) the time interval during which P is more than $78.4\,\mathrm{m}$ above the ground.
                                                                    (4 marks)

   (b) State the modelling assumption you have made in your solution about the motion of P.
                                                                            (1 mark)

10. A particle Q moves in a horizontal plane so that at time t, $t \geqslant 0$, its position vector $\mathbf{r}$ referred to a fixed origin O is given by

    $$\mathbf{r} = (t - 2\cos t)\mathbf{i} + (2\sin t)\mathbf{j}$$

    (a) For the interval $0 \leqslant t \leqslant 2\pi$, find
        (i) the value of t when the speed of P is least,   **(7 marks)**

        (ii) the position vector of P at this instant.   **(2 marks)**

    (b) Show that the magnitude of the force acting on P is constant.   **(4 marks)**

    Total: 100 marks

Longman Examination Board

General Certificate of Education

Pure Mathematics and Mechanics

Paper 8 (Mechanics)

Time: 2 hours

Instructions

■ Answer all questions.

■ Make sure your method is clear, with sufficient working to show how the answer has been obtained.

■ Wherever possible, draw diagrams to support your answer.

Information for candidates

■ The number of marks is given in brackets at the end of each question or part-question.

■ Take g to be $9.8\,\text{ms}^{-2}$.

■ This paper has 10 questions. The maximum mark for this paper is 100.

Number	Mark
1.	
2.	
3.	
4.	
5.	
6.	
7.	
8.	
9.	
10.	
Total:	

---

1. Two athletes support a uniform pole XY of mass 31 kg and length 12 m horizontally on their shoulders at the points A and B, as shown below.

A load of mass 80 kg is suspended from the point C of the pole; $XA = 1\,\text{m}$, $BY = 1.5\,\text{m}$ and $XC = 5\,\text{m}$.

Find, in N, the vertical force exerted by the loaded pole on each man's shoulder.

(5 marks)

2. A car is moving with uniform acceleration along a straight road. The car passes checkpoints A and B when moving at speeds of $22\,\text{ms}^{-1}$ and $40\,\text{ms}^{-1}$. Find, in ms^{-1} to 1 decimal place, the speed of the car at the point C, where C is the mid-point of AB. **(6 marks)**

3. A lorry of mass 10 000 kg has a maximum speed of $12\,\text{ms}^{-1}$ up a slope inclined at $\arcsin 0.15$ to the horizontal against non-gravitational resistive forces totalling 9860 N.

   (a) Find, to the nearest kW, the effective power of the engine in this situation. **(4 marks)**

   The lorry now pulls a trailer of mass 6500 kg along a straight horizontal road with constant acceleration $0.13\,\text{ms}^{-2}$. The trailer is connected to the lorry by a light horizontal tow-bar and the resistances for the trailer total 5450 N.

   (b) Calculate the tension in the tow-bar. **(3 marks)**

Turn over

21

4. The foot of a uniform ladder of mass M and length $2a$ rests on horizontal ground where the coefficient of friction between the ladder and the ground is 0.65. The top of the ladder rests against a smooth vertical wall. Given that equilibrium is limiting when a body of mass $2M$ is hung from the top of the ladder and the inclination of the ladder to the horizontal is θ,

    (a) find

        (i)   the magnitude of the force exerted on the ladder by the wall, giving your answer in terms of M and g,   **(4 marks)**

        (ii) the size of θ to the nearest degree.   **(4 marks)**

    (b) Explain how you have modelled the ladder in your solution.   **(1 mark)**

5. Three small marbles, A, B and C, of equal mass and radius, lie at rest on a smooth horizontal floor with their centres in a straight line. A is projected towards B and after the collision, B goes on to collide with C. The coefficient of restitution between A and B is e, and the coefficient of restitution between B and C is E. Show that A and B will collide just once if

$$E < \frac{3e - 1}{e + 1}$$

                                                                                          (11 marks)

6. A particle P of mass m is connected by a light inextensible string of length $4a$ to a fixed point A and by another light inextensible string of length $3a$ to a fixed point B. The point B is at a distance $5a$ vertically below A, as shown in the diagram below.

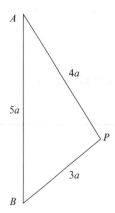

    The particle P moves in a horizontal circle about AB with constant angular speed ω. Given that both strings are taut, show that

$$\omega^2 \geqslant \frac{5g}{16a}$$

                                                                                          (11 marks)

7. (a) Use integration to show that the centre of mass of a uniform semicircular lamina, of radius a, is at a distance of $4a/(3\pi)$ from the centre of the bounding diameter.

                                                                                          (6 marks)

    (b) A uniform lamina L is cut out, as shown in the diagram below, and consists of a semicircle and a rectangle. The semicircle is of radius 20 cm and the breadth of the rectangle is b cm.

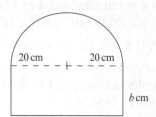

        Given that the centre of mass of L is on the bounding diameter of the semicircle, find the value of b to 2 decimal places.   **(6 marks)**

8. A fixed rough plane is inclined at 30° to the horizontal. A body of mass 2 kg is placed on the plane and a variable force of magnitude P newtons is applied to the body directly up the plane along the line of greatest slope. The coefficient of friction between the body and the plane is 0.2.

   (a) By modelling the body as a particle, find the value of P to 2 decimal places when it is in limiting equilibrium and on the point of moving

      (i) up the plane,   **(5 marks)**

      (ii) down the plane.   **(3 marks)**

   The force P is removed and the particle is released from rest and moves down the plane.

   (b) Find the speed of the particle after it has moved through a distance of 1.2 m down the plane.   **(4 marks)**

9. On a certain day, low water for a harbour mouth is at noon, and high water at 1820; the corresponding depths of water being 5 m and 12 m, respectively.

   Student A models the approximate rise of the water level to be at constant speed.

   (a) Find the earliest time when a boat drawing 9 m of water could enter the harbour using this model.   **(4 marks)**

   Student B finds the approximate rise in water level using a simple harmonic model.

   (b) Find the earliest time of entry possible for the same boat using this model.

         (7 marks)

   (c) Comment briefly on your findings.   **(2 marks)**

10. A particle P of mass m is attached by a light elastic string of natural length L to a fixed point O and allowed to fall freely from rest at O. When the particle reaches its lowest position and is at instantaneous rest, it is at a distance $2L$ below O.

    (a) Find, in terms of m and g, the tension in the string at this instant of greatest extension.

          (6 marks)

    (b) Find, in terms of L, the distance below O at which P acquires its greatest speed.

          (3 marks)

    (c) Find, in terms of L and g, the greatest speed of P during its descent.   **(5 marks)**

Total: 100 marks

Solutions to practice exam papers

An explanation of the marking system is given at the front of the book.

In the solutions to the Mechanics practice exam papers (Papers 5–8), the topic being examined is identified in each case.

Use the following solutions to mark your papers, then look at the mark analysis on page iv.

Solutions to Paper 1 (Pure Mathematics)

Note: Remember to give the final answer to each question as required by the examiner.

1. $\sin x = \pm 0.6325$

    $x = 39°, 141°, 219°, 321°$

    B1 any one correct; **B1** a further one correct; **B1** all four correct   **3 marks**

> **TIP**
>
> Notice the $\pm$ sign.

2. Obtaining $2x^2 - 3x - 5$ **B1**

    Factors $(2x - 5)(x + 1)$ *OR* $-1, \frac{5}{2}$ are critical values   **M1**

    $-1 \leqslant x \leqslant \frac{5}{2}$ is the solution set   **A1 A1**   **4 marks**

> **TIP**
>
> To obtain the solution set, consider the intervals $x < -1$, $-1 \leqslant x \leqslant \frac{5}{2}$, $x > \frac{5}{2}$ and the sign of $2x^2 - 3x - 5$ in each of these.
> Always look for the critical values.

3. (a) $u_1 = 1, u_2 = -1$ **B1**

    $u_3 = 1, u_4 = -1$ **B1**   **2 marks**

    (b) $\displaystyle\sum_{r=1}^{n} u_r = 1$ when r is odd   **B1**   **1 mark**

    (c) The sequence oscillates between -1 and 1 and is called a finite oscillating sequence.   **B1**   **1 mark**

4. $\displaystyle\int (x^{\frac{1}{2}} - x^{-\frac{3}{2}})\,dx = \frac{2}{3}x^{\frac{3}{2}} + 2x^{-\frac{1}{2}}$ **M1 A1 A1**

    $\left[\dfrac{2}{3}x^{\frac{3}{2}} + 2x^{-\frac{1}{2}}\right]_4^{16} = \dfrac{128}{3} + \dfrac{1}{2} - \left(\dfrac{16}{3} + 1\right)$ **M1**

    $= 36\frac{5}{6}$ **A1**   **5 marks**

> **TIP**
>
> Use $\displaystyle\int x^n\,dx = \frac{1}{n+1}x^{n+1}$

5. (a) Note that the three probabilities add up to 1; so $p = 1 - \frac{2}{5} - \frac{1}{3} = \frac{4}{15}$ **B1**   **1 mark**

    (b) (i) $p(\text{win–draw } or \text{ draw–win}) = 2 \times \dfrac{2}{5} \times \dfrac{4}{15} = \dfrac{16}{75}$ **M1 A1**   **2 marks**

(ii) p(win–win *or* lose–lose *or* draw–draw) $= \left(\dfrac{2}{5}\right)^2 + \left(\dfrac{1}{3}\right)^2 + \left(\dfrac{4}{15}\right)^2$ **M1**

$$= \frac{77}{225}$$ **A1**   **2 marks**

TIP

Draw a tree diagram to help you to build the solution.

6.   Note that $8.65 \leqslant r < 8.75$.

(a)   Smallest circumference $= 2 \times 8.65 \times \pi\,\text{cm}$ **M1**

$$= 54.35\,\text{cm (2 d.p.)}$$ **A1**   **2 marks**

(b)   Measured value for area $= \pi \times 8.7^2\,\text{cm}^2$ **M1**

Greatest possible area $= \pi \times 8.75^2\,\text{cm}^2$ **M1**

Greatest absolute error $= \pi(8.75^2 - 8.7^2)\,\text{cm}^2$ **M1**

$$= 2.74\,\text{cm}^2\ (2\ \text{d.p.})$$ **A1**   **4 marks**

TIP

Notice the limits for r.

7. $t = e^x$ then $t^2 = e^{2x}$ and equation is

$3t^2 - 7t + 2 = 0$ **B1**

$(3t - 1)(t - 2) = 0$ **M1**

Hence $t = \frac{1}{3}$ or $t = 2$ **A1**

$e^x = \frac{1}{3}$ or $e^x = 2$ **A1**

$x = -\ln 3$ or $x = \ln 2$ **M1**

$= -1.099,\ 0.693\ (3\ \text{d.p.})$ **A1 A1**   **7 marks**

TIP

Use the hint and take $t = e^x$.

8. $y = \dfrac{x^2}{x + 2}$

Using the quotient formula for differentiation we have

$$\frac{dy}{dx} = \frac{(x + 2)\dfrac{d}{dx}(x^2) - x^2\dfrac{d}{dx}(x + 2)}{(x + 2)^2}$$ **M1**

$$= \frac{2x(x + 2) - x^2}{(x + 2)^2} = \frac{x^2 + 4x}{(x + 2)^2}$$ **A1**

At $x = 4$, $y = \dfrac{8}{3}$ **B1**

$\dfrac{dy}{dx} = \dfrac{8}{9}$ **A1**

Gradient of normal at $(4, \frac{8}{3})$ is $-\dfrac{9}{8}$ **M1**

Equation of normal $y - \frac{8}{3} = -\frac{9}{8}(x - 4)$ **M1 A1**   **7 marks**

TIP

> Identify the quotient and use the formula.
> When writing down the equation of a tangent or normal always use the form
> $y - y_1 = m(x - x_1)$ and NOT $y = mx + c$ because it saves time and is less prone to error.

9. (a) $AB^2 = (1 - 5)^2 + (2 - 3)^2 + (4 - 7)^2 = 26$

$AC^2 = (1 - 3)^2 + (2 - 7)^2 + (4 - 4)^2 = 29$

$BC^2 = (5 - 3)^2 + (3 - 7)^2 + (7 - 4)^2 = 29$ **M1**

$AB = \sqrt{26}, AC = \sqrt{29}, BC = \sqrt{29}$ **A1 A1 A1**   **4 marks**

(b) Note that the triangle is isosceles, as shown in the diagram.

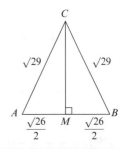

$AM = \frac{1}{2}\sqrt{26}$ **B1**

$\cos \widehat{BAC} = \dfrac{\frac{1}{2}\sqrt{26}}{\sqrt{29}}$ **M1**

$\widehat{BAC} = 61.7°$ (to the nearest $0.1°$)   **A1**   **3 marks**

TIP

> Recall the formula $d^2 = (x_1 - x_2)^2 + (y_1 - y_2)^2 + (z_1 - z_2)^2$.
> You could also use the cosine rule to find the angle, but it is longer.

10. (a) Consider one circle, as shown, centre C_1, common chord AB, second circle centre C_2, shown. $\triangle C_1 A C_2$ is equilateral, so

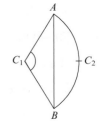

$\angle AC_1B = 120° \equiv \dfrac{2\pi}{3}$ radians   **B1**

length of arc $AC_2B = a \times \dfrac{2\pi}{3}$ **M1**

perimeter of shaded region $= \dfrac{4a\pi}{3}$ **A1**   **3 marks**

(b) Area of sector $C_1AB = \dfrac{1}{2} \times \dfrac{2\pi}{3} \times a^2$ **M1**

Area of $\triangle C_1AB = \dfrac{1}{2} a^2 \sin \dfrac{2\pi}{3} = \dfrac{1}{2} a^2 \times \dfrac{\sqrt{3}}{2}$ **M1 A1**

Area of segment $AC_2B = \dfrac{\pi}{3} a^2 - \dfrac{a^2 \sqrt{3}}{4}$ **M1**

Shaded area is double this $= a^2 \left(\dfrac{2\pi}{3} - \dfrac{\sqrt{3}}{2} \right)$ **A1**   **5 marks**

TIP

> (a) Draw a sketch, recall $l = r\theta$,
> (b) Recall $A = \frac{1}{2}r^2\theta$.

11. (a) $\dfrac{1 - 5\sin x \cos x + 2\sin^2 x}{\cos^2 x}$

$= \dfrac{\cos^2 x + \sin^2 x - 5\sin x \cos x + 2\sin^2 x}{\cos^2 x}$ **M1**

$= 1 + \tan^2 x - 5\tan x + 2\tan^2 x$ **M1**

$= 3\tan^2 x - 5\tan x + 1$ **A1**   **3 marks**

(b) $3\tan^2 x - 5\tan x + 1 = 0$

$$\tan x = \frac{5 \pm \sqrt{25 - 4 \times 3 \times 1}}{6} \qquad \textbf{M1}$$

$$= \frac{5 + \sqrt{13}}{6} \quad \text{or} \quad \frac{5 - \sqrt{13}}{6} \qquad \textbf{A1} \quad \textbf{A1}$$

$55.1°$ or $235.1°$, $13.1°$ or $193.1°$ **A1**   **M1**   **A1**   **6 marks**

TIP

Recall that $\cos^2 x + \sin^2 x \equiv 1$

$$\frac{\sin x}{\cos x} \equiv \tan x$$

Notice how the identities $\cos^2 x + \sin^2 x = 1$ and $\dfrac{\sin x}{\cos x} = \tan x$ are used in the proof.

---

12. $f(x) = x^3 - 7x + 4$

(a) $f(-3) = -27 + 21 + 4 = -2$ **M1**

$f(-2) = -8 + 14 + 4 = 10$ **A1**

Sign changes and f is continuous. $\therefore y = f(x)$ crosses x-axis in $(-3, -2)$ and a root exists.   **A1**   **3 marks**

(b) In linear interpolation, we need to find where the line joining $(-3, -2)$ and $(-2, 10)$ crosses the x-axis.   **M1**

$$\frac{\alpha}{2} = \frac{1 - \alpha}{10} \quad \Rightarrow \quad 12\alpha = 2$$

$\alpha = 0.167$ **M1**   **A1**

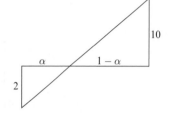

So an estimate of the root is -2.833 **A1**   **4 marks**

(c) A systematic search over the values of $f(0), f(1), \dots$, shows the $f(0) > 0$, $f(1) < 0$, $f(2) < 0$, $f(3) > 0$ **M1**

So $n = 1$ and $n = 3$ due to sign changes.   **A1**   **A1**   **3 marks**

TIP

(a) Look for sign change.

(c) Look again for a sign change.

---

13. (a) Area of R needs $\displaystyle\int (4 + \sin 2x)\, dx$ **M1**

$$= [4x - \tfrac{1}{2}\cos 2x] \qquad \textbf{M1} \qquad \textbf{A1}$$

$$\text{Area of } R = [4x - \tfrac{1}{2}\cos 2x]_0^{\pi/2} = 2\pi + \tfrac{1}{2} - (-\tfrac{1}{2}) \qquad \textbf{M1}$$

$$= 2\pi + 1 \qquad \textbf{A1} \qquad \textbf{5 marks}$$

(b) Volume generated needs $\displaystyle\int (4 + \sin 2x)^2\, dx$ **M1**

$$= \int (16 + 8\sin 2x + \sin^2 2x)\, dx \qquad \textbf{A1}$$

$$\int \sin^2 2x\, dx = \frac{1}{2}\int (1 - \cos 4x)\, dx = \frac{x}{2} - \frac{1}{8}\sin 4x \qquad \textbf{M1} \quad \textbf{A1}$$

$$\int (4 + \sin^2 2x)\, dx = 16x - 4\cos 2x + \frac{x}{2} - \frac{1}{8}\sin 4x$$

$$\text{Volume} = \pi[\quad]_0^{\pi/2} = \pi\left(8\pi + 4 + \frac{\pi}{4} - 0 - (0 - 4 + 0 - 0)\right) \qquad \textbf{M1}$$

$$= \frac{\pi}{4}(33\pi + 32) \qquad \textbf{A1} \qquad \textbf{6 marks}$$

TIP

(a) Use Area $= \int y\,dx$.

(b) Use Volume $= \pi \int y^2\,dx$.

14. (a) At stationary points $f'(x) = 0$, so we have:

At $x = 1$, $3 + p + q = 0$ **M1**

$x = -3$, $27 - 3p + q = 0$ **A1**

Solving for p and q gives $p = 6$, $q = -9$ **M1 A1** **4 marks**

(b) $3x^2 + 6x - 9 < 0$ **M1**

$3(x + 3)(x - 1) < 0$ **A1**

$\Rightarrow \quad -3 < x < 1$ **A1 A1** **4 marks**

(c) $f(x) = \displaystyle\int f'(x)\,dx + C = \int (3x^2 + 6x - 9)\,dx + C$

$= x^3 + 3x^2 - 9x + 5$ because $f(1) = 0$ **M1 A1**

$= (x - 1)[x^2 + 4x - 5]$ **M1**

$= (x - 1)^2(x + 5)$ **A1** **4 marks**

(d)

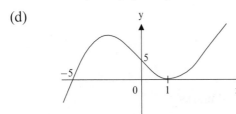

B1 B1 **2 marks**

TIP

(b) Function is decreasing when $f'(x) < 0$.

(c) Note how to evaluate the constant C.

Solutions to Paper 2 (Pure Mathematics)

1. We have a geometric series with first term 100 and ratio 1.02 with 26 terms

$$\text{Sum} = \frac{100[(1.02)^{26} - 1]}{1.02 - 1} \qquad \textbf{M1 A1}$$

$$= £3367.09 \qquad \textbf{A1} \qquad \textbf{3 marks}$$

TIP

Use your data booklet for the formula.

2. Considering the mark distribution in order of size, the median is the mean of the 15th and 16th terms, both of which are 7 marks. $\therefore$ Median $= 7$ marks **B1**

The upper quantile is 8 and the lower quantile is 3. **B1 B1**

Interquantile range is $8 - 3 = 5$ **B1** **4 marks**

TIP

Median is in the middle.

3. Let $y = e^{2x} - 3$

    $e^{2x} = y + 3$

    $2x = \ln(y + 3)$

    $x = \frac{1}{2}\ln(y + 3)$ **M1   A1**

    Change over x and y

    $y = \frac{1}{2}\ln(x + 3)$

    $f^{-1}: \quad x \mapsto \frac{1}{2}\ln(x + 3)$ **A1**

    Domain is all real $x > -3$.   **B1   4 marks**

 TIP

> Note the standard method for finding the inverse.

4. Using the formula for the sum of n terms of an arithmetic series, we have $a = 38$, $d = -2$, $S_n = 378$

    $\frac{n}{2}[76 - 2(n - 1)] = 378$ **M1**

    Equation reduces to $n^2 - 39n + 378 = 0$ **A1**

    Solving by factors or formula $(n - 18)(n - 21) = 0$ **M1**

    $n = 18$ or $n = 21$ **A1**

    $n = 18$ is value required because $n = 21$ has negative terms.

    ANS.   18 days to dig well.   **A1   5 marks**

TIP

> Use your data booklet for the formula.

5. Take $u = \ln x$ and $\dfrac{dv}{dx} = x$

    $\dfrac{du}{dx} = \dfrac{1}{x}$ and $v = \dfrac{x^2}{2}$

    Parts formula is $\displaystyle\int u\,\frac{dv}{dx}\,dx = uv - \int v\,\frac{du}{dx}\,dx$

    $\displaystyle\int x\ln x\,dx = \frac{x^2}{2}\ln x - \int \frac{x^2}{2}\cdot\frac{1}{x}\,dx$ **M1   A1**

    $\displaystyle \qquad\qquad = \frac{x^2}{2}\ln x - \frac{1}{4}x^2$ **A1**

    $\displaystyle\int_1^2 x\ln x\,dx = \left[\frac{x^2}{2}\ln x - \frac{1}{4}x^2\right]_1^2$

    $\displaystyle \qquad\qquad = 2\ln 2 - 1 - \left(0 - \frac{1}{4}\right)$ **M1**

    $\displaystyle \qquad\qquad = 2\ln 2 - \frac{3}{4}.$ **A1   5 marks**

TIP

> Recognise that integration by parts is needed.
> Notice the form required for the answer.

6. Substitute $3x + 1$ for y in the equation

$x^2 + y^2 = 17$

$x^2 + (3x + 1)^2 = 17$ **M1**

$10x^2 + 6x - 16 = 0.$

That is $5x^2 + 3x - 8 = 0.$ **A1**

Factors or formulae $(x - 1)(5x + 8)$ $\left(\text{or } \dfrac{-3 \pm \sqrt{9 + 160}}{10} \right)$ **M1**

$x = 1$ or $x = -1.6$ **A1**

$y = 4$ or $y = -3.8.$

So we require $(1, 4)$ and $(-1.6, -3.8).$ **A1**   **5 marks**

TIP

> Eliminate y.
> Factors are best if you can find them easily.

7. Differentiating with respect to x

$3y^2 \dfrac{dy}{dx} + 6x^2 + 12x = 0$ **M1** **A1**

At $(1, -2)$, $\dfrac{dy}{dx} = -\dfrac{18}{12} = -\dfrac{3}{2} = \text{gradient of tangent.}$ **M1** **A1**

Equation of tangent $y + 2 = -\frac{3}{2}(x - 1)$ **M1** **A1**   **6 marks**

TIP

> Chain rule needed to differentiate y^3 with respect to x.

8. (a) $(1 + 2x)^{\frac{1}{2}} = 1 + \frac{1}{2}(2x) + \dfrac{\frac{1}{2}(\frac{1}{2} - 1)}{2!}(2x)^2 + \dfrac{\frac{1}{2}(\frac{1}{2} - 1)(\frac{1}{2} - 2)}{3!}(2x)^3$ **M1** **A1**

   $= 1 + x - \frac{1}{2}x^2 + \frac{1}{2}x^3.$ **M1**   **A1**   **4 marks**

   (b) Length is given by $L = 100(1 + 0.017 - \frac{1}{2}(0.017)^2)$ **M1**

   $= 101.686$ (to 3 decimal places)   **A1**   **2 marks**

TIP

> Use data booklet for binomial series.

9. (a) The equation of l_1 is $y - 2 = \frac{2}{3}(x + 3)$ **M1**   **A1**   **2 marks**

   (b) At A, $x = 0$ and $y = 2 + \frac{2}{3}(3) = 4$

   A is $(0, 4)$.   **B1**

   The line l_2 has gradient $-\frac{3}{2}$ and passes through A **M1**

   so its equation is $y - 4 = -\frac{3}{2}x.$ **A1**   **3 marks**

   (c) l_2 meets x-axis when $y = 0$, so B has coordinates $(\frac{8}{3}, 0)$.   **B1**

   $AB^2 = 4^2 + \left(\dfrac{8}{3}\right)^2$ (Pythagoras)   **M1**

$$AB = \frac{\sqrt{208}}{3} = \frac{4\sqrt{13}}{3}.$$ **A1**   **3 marks**

TIP

Sketch a diagram showing l_1 and l_2.

10. (a) $\tan\theta = \frac{4}{3}$; consider $3, 4, 5\triangle$ as shown in the diagram.

So $\sin\theta = \frac{4}{5}$ and $\cos\theta = \frac{3}{5}$.   **B1   B1**   **2 marks**

(b) $5\cos(2x - \theta) = 5\cos 2x \cos\theta + 5\sin 2x \sin\theta$

$$= 5\cos 2x \left(\frac{3}{5}\right) + 5\sin 2x \left(\frac{4}{5}\right) \quad \textbf{M1}$$

$$= 3\cos 2x + 4\sin 2x, \text{ as required} \quad \textbf{A1} \quad \textbf{2 marks}$$

(c) $\sin\theta = \frac{4}{5}$, so $\theta = 0.9273$ radians.   **B1**

We need to solve $\cos(2x - 0.9273) = -0.2$

$2x = 1.7722 + 0.9273 \ \Rightarrow \ x = 1.35$ (2 d.p.)   **M1   A1**

$2x = -1.7722 + 0.9273 \ \Rightarrow \ x = -0.42$ (2 d.p.).   **M1   A1**   **5 marks**

TIP

Notice the two possibilities in the interval $\left[-\dfrac{\pi}{2}, \dfrac{\pi}{2}\right]$.

11. (a) Shaded segment shown is $\frac{1}{4}$ area of circle. Let circle have radius a and θ is, as shown in the diagram.

Area of shaded segment = area of sector − area of $\triangle$

$$= \frac{1}{2}a^2\theta - \frac{1}{2}a^2\sin\theta \quad \textbf{M1 \ A1}$$

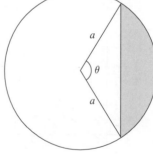

So $\dfrac{1}{2}a^2\theta - \dfrac{1}{2}a^2\sin\theta = \dfrac{\pi}{4}a^2$ **M1**

which reduces to give equation $\theta - \sin\theta - \dfrac{\pi}{2} = 0$.   **A1**   **4 marks**

(b) With $f(\theta) \equiv \theta - \sin\theta - \dfrac{\pi}{2}$

$f(2.2) = -0.1793 < 0$

$f(2.4) = 0.1537 > 0$.   **M1**

Continuous function f and sign change implies that a root lies in $[2.2, 2.4]$.
   A1   **2 marks**

(c) Consider the interval $[2.305, 2.315]$ which spans value 2.31:   **M1**

$f(2.305) = -0.00816 < 0$

$f(2.315) = 0.00856 > 0$ **M1**

$\therefore p$ is 2.31 correct to 2 decimal places.   **A1**   **3 marks**

TIP

(a)   Use a clear diagram.
(c)   Look for sign change to check accuracy of your answer.

12. (a) $x = A(B^t)$

$\ln x = \ln[A(B^t)] = \ln A + \ln B^t$ **M1   A1**

Hence $\ln x = t \ln B + \ln A$ **A1**

(logs to base 10 could equally well be taken).

t	2	5	10	20	30
$\ln x$	7.27	7.81	8.72	10.55	12.37

We now plot $\ln x$ against t as shown on the graph.   **M1**

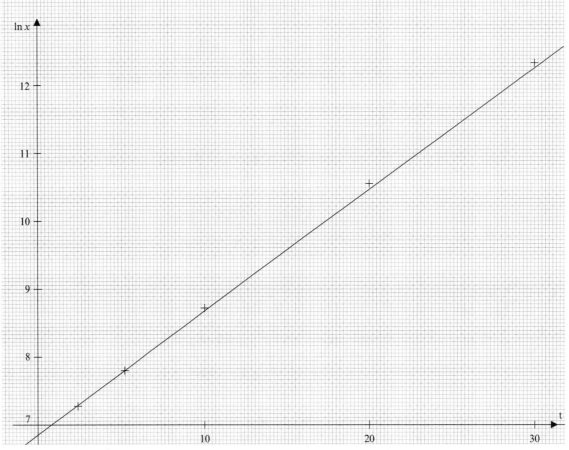

Straight line obtained so relation confirmed.   **M1   A1   6 marks**

(b) On $t = 0$ axis, $\ln x \approx 6.85 = \ln A \Rightarrow A = 990$ (to 2 significant figures)   **M1   A1**

Gradient of line $= \ln B \approx \dfrac{12.3 - 6.9}{30} \approx 5.4$

$B = 1.2$ (to 2 significant figures).   **M1   A1   4 marks**

> **TIP**
>
> After taking logs appreciate that from the straight line, log B is the gradient and log A is the y-intercept.

13. (a) Suppose that the cylinder is of height h cm, then $\pi x^2 h = 2000$.   **B1**

Also $A = \pi x^2 + \pi x^2 + 2\pi x h$ **M1**

$= 2\pi x^2 + 2\pi x \left(\dfrac{2000}{x^2 \pi}\right)$

$= 2\pi x^2 + \dfrac{4000}{x}$.   **M1   A1   4 marks**

(b) $\dfrac{\mathrm{d}A}{\mathrm{d}x} = 4\pi x - \dfrac{4000}{x^2}.$ **M1   A1**

For a stationary value of A, $4\pi x - \dfrac{4000}{x^2} = 0$ **M1**

$x^3 = \dfrac{1000}{\pi}$ **A1**

That is $x = \dfrac{10}{\pi^{1/3}} = 10\pi^{-\frac{1}{3}}$ **A1**

$\dfrac{\mathrm{d}^2A}{\mathrm{d}x^2} = 4\pi + \dfrac{8000}{x^3} > 0$ when $x = 10\pi^{-\frac{1}{3}}$ **M1**

so the value of A is a minimum.   **6 marks**

(c)   Minimum value of $A = 2\pi \times 100\pi^{-\frac{1}{3}} + \dfrac{4000}{10\pi^{-\frac{1}{3}}} = 6.83\,\text{cm}^2.$ **M1   A1**   **2 marks**

TIP

(a)   Know the formulae for a cylinder's surface area and volume.
(b)   Notice how to confirm the minimum.

---

14. (a)   First we need to find the coordinates of Q.

$\dfrac{\mathrm{d}x}{\mathrm{d}t} = 2t, \qquad \dfrac{\mathrm{d}y}{\mathrm{d}t} = 3t^2 \;\Rightarrow\; \dfrac{\mathrm{d}y}{\mathrm{d}x} = \dfrac{3t^2}{2t} = \dfrac{3t}{2}.$ **M1   A1**

At P, $t = 2$, $x = 4$, $y = 8$ and $\dfrac{\mathrm{d}y}{\mathrm{d}x} = 3.$

Gradient of normal is $-\frac{1}{3}$ at P and its equation is $y - 8 = -\frac{1}{3}(x - 4)$ **M1   A1**

Q is the point where $y = 0$, that is $(28, 0)$.   **A1**

Area of $R = \displaystyle\int y \dfrac{\mathrm{d}x}{\mathrm{d}t}\,\mathrm{d}t \left(\begin{matrix}\text{under}\\\text{curve}\end{matrix}\right) + \triangle$ **M1**

$= \displaystyle\int_0^2 2t^4\,\mathrm{d}t + \dfrac{1}{2} \times 24 \times 8$ **B1**

$= \left[\dfrac{2}{5}t^5\right]_0^2 + 96 = \dfrac{64}{5} + 96 = 108\,\dfrac{4}{5}.$ **A1   A1**   **9 marks**

(b)   Volume of $S = \pi \displaystyle\int y^2 \dfrac{\mathrm{d}x}{\mathrm{d}t}\,\mathrm{d}t + \text{Cone}$ **M1**

$= \pi \displaystyle\int_0^2 2t^7\,\mathrm{d}t + \dfrac{\pi}{3} \times 8^2 \times 24$ **A1   A1**

$= \pi \left[\dfrac{t^8}{4}\right]_0^2 + 512\pi$

$= 64\pi + 512\pi = 576\pi$ **A1   A1**   **5 marks**

TIP

Notice the formulae for area and volume in terms of t.

Solutions to Paper 3 (Pure Mathematics)

1. (a) $(1 - 2x)^6 = (1 - 12x), +60x^2, -160x^3.$ **B1**   **B1**   **B1**   **3 marks**

    (b) $(2 + x)(1 - 12x + 60x^2 - 160x^3, \ldots)$

        $= (2 - 23x), +108x^2 - 260x^3, \ldots$ **B1**   **B1**   **B1**   **3 marks**

> **TIP**
>
> When multiplying out brackets do it constructively and do not cut corners. This way you will make fewer errors.

2. (a) $ar^4 = \frac{1}{8}, ar^7 = -\frac{1}{64} \Rightarrow r^3 = -\frac{1}{8}$ $r = -\frac{1}{2}$ **M1**   **A1**   **A1**

    Substitute $a = 2$.   **A1**   **4 marks**

    (b) $S_7 = \dfrac{2[1 - (-\frac{1}{2})^7]}{1 - (-\frac{1}{2})} = \dfrac{4}{3}\left(1 + \dfrac{1}{128}\right) = 1\frac{11}{32}.$ **M1**   **A1**   **2 marks**

> **TIP**
>
> Use nth term $= ar^{n-1}$.

3. (a) $f(-2) = -8 + 56 - 48 = 0 \Rightarrow (x + 2)$ is a factor   **B1**

       $(x + 2)(x^2 - 2x - 24) = (x + 2)(x + 4)(x - 6).$ **M1**   **A1**   **3 marks**

       To find the partial fraction you can either use the 'cover-up' rule or consider

$$\frac{A}{x + 2} + \frac{B}{x + 4} + \frac{C}{x - 6}.$$

    (b) $\dfrac{8}{(x + 2)(x + 4)(x - 6)} = \dfrac{-5}{x + 2} + \dfrac{4}{x + 4} + \dfrac{1}{x - 6}.$ **B1**   **B1**   **B1**   **3 marks**

> **TIP**
>
> When factorising $(x + 2)(x^2 - 2x - 24)$, the best method is to fix the x^2 and -24 by considering the x^3 and -48 terms; the x term $-2x$ can then be obtained easily by considering the x term, $(-28x)$ or the x^2 term, $(0x^2)$, in the original expression. Use this method because it leads to less errors than the method of long division.

4. (a) Sketch   **B2**   **2 marks**

    (b) Straight line   **B1**   **1 mark**

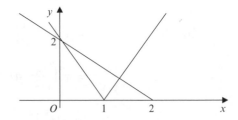

    (c) (i) $\left.\begin{array}{l} y = 2 - x \\ y = 2x - 2 \end{array}\right\}$ Intersect $\Rightarrow O = 3x - 4x \Rightarrow x = \frac{4}{3}$ **M1**

          $\Rightarrow$ Points of Intersection at $x = 0, x = \frac{4}{3}$ **A1**   **2 marks**

       (ii) $x \leqslant 0 \bigcup x \geqslant \frac{4}{3}.$ **A1**   **A1**   **2 marks**

> **TIP**
>
> (a) Draw a careful sketch.
> (c) Do NOT write your final answer as $0 \geqslant x \geqslant \frac{4}{3}$ as this implies $0 \geqslant \frac{4}{3}$. It could cost you an A1 mark.

5. (a)   Range $\Rightarrow y \in \mathbb{R}$.   **B1**   **1 mark**

   (b)   Curve $y = f(x)$ **B1**

   coordinates   **B1**   **2 marks**

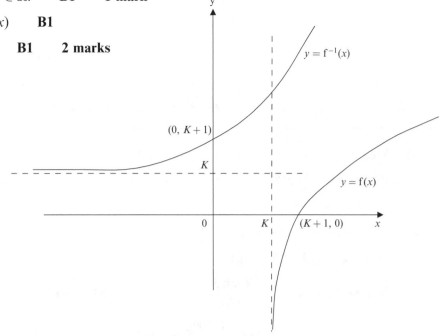

   (c)   Inverse $x = \ln(y - K) \Rightarrow e^x = y - K$ **M1**   **A1**

   $\Rightarrow f^{-1}: x \mapsto e^x + K$ **A1**

   Domain $x \in \mathbb{R}$, Range $y > K$.   **A1**   **4 marks**

   (d)   Curve $y = f^{-1}x$ **B1**

   coordinates   **B1**   **2 marks**

TIP

Answer all the demands for parts (b) and (d) *on the graphs*.

6. (a)   Gradient at $(-1, -2)$ is $-2 \Rightarrow -2 = K(1 + 1)(-2 + 3)$ **M1**

   $\Rightarrow K = -1$.   **A1**   **2 marks**

   (b) $\dfrac{dy}{dx} = -1(3 - x - 2x^2) \Rightarrow y = -3x + \frac{1}{2}x^2 + \frac{2}{3}x^3 + C$ **M1**   **A1**

   Passes through $(-1, -2) \Rightarrow -2 = 3 + \frac{1}{2} - \frac{2}{3} + C$ **M1**

   $\Rightarrow C = -4\frac{5}{6}$

   $y = \frac{2}{3}x^3 + \frac{1}{2}x^2 - 3x - 4\frac{5}{6}$.   **A1**   **4 marks**

   (c)   Gradient of normal at $(-1, -2) = \frac{1}{2}$ **B1**

   $\Rightarrow$ Equation of normal at $(-1, -2)$ is $y + 2 = \frac{1}{2}(x + 1)$.   **M1**   **A1**   **3 marks**

TIP

   (b)   Use integration to move from $\dfrac{dy}{dx}$ to y.

   (c)   As you are not asked to express this equation in its simplest form there is no need to collect the constant terms.

7. (a) $t = 20, 0.6A = Ae^{-20K} \Rightarrow -20K = \ln(0.6)$ **M1**   **A1**

   $\Rightarrow K = \dfrac{1}{20}\ln\left(\dfrac{5}{3}\right) \Rightarrow K = 0.0255$.   **A1**   **3 marks**

(b) (i) $e^{-0.0255t} = \frac{1}{2} \Rightarrow 0.0255t = \ln 2$ **M1**   **A1**

$t = 27.1$ **A1**   **3 marks**

(ii) $\dfrac{m}{A} = e^{-0.0255 \times 40} = 0.361.$ **M1**   **A1**   **A1**   **3 marks**

TIP

Be prepared to use *both* log and exponential forms of equations.

8. (a) Area of $\triangle OPQ = \frac{1}{2} \times 4^2 \sin \theta$ **M1**   **A1**

$\Rightarrow (8 \sin \theta - \frac{1}{2} \cdot 2^2 \theta) = \frac{1}{15} \pi \cdot 4^2$ **A1**   **M1**

$\Rightarrow 60 \sin \theta - 15\theta - 8\pi = 0.$ **A1**   **5 marks**

(b) $f(\theta) = 60 \sin \theta - 15\theta - 8\pi$

$f'(\theta) = 60 \cos \theta - 15$ **B1**

Second Approx $= \dfrac{\pi}{5} - \dfrac{60 \sin 36° - 3\pi - 8\pi}{60 \cos 36° - 15}$ **M1**   **A1**

$= 0.6283 - \dfrac{0.7096}{33.541} = 0.607$

≈ 0.61 (2 d.p.)   **A1**   **4 marks**

TIP

Use the Newton–Raphson iterative process from your data book.

9. (a)   **M1**   **A1**   **A1**   **A1**   **A1**   **5 marks**

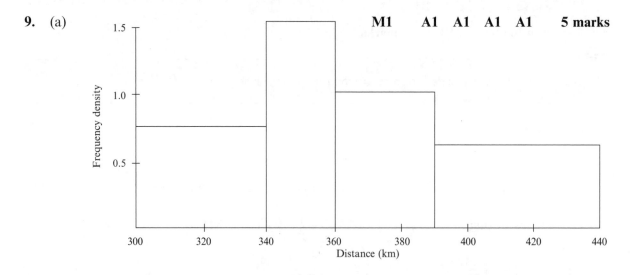

(b) Mean $= (320 \times 30 + 350 \times 30 + 375 \times 30 + 415 \times 30) \cdot \dfrac{1}{120}$ **M1**

$= 365$ **A1**

Variance $= \dfrac{30}{120} [(365 - 320)^2 + (365 - 350)^2 + (375 - 365)^2 + (415 - 365)^2]$ **M1**

$= 1212.5$ **A1**

Standard Deviation $= \sqrt{} = 34.8$ **A1**   **5 marks**

TIP

(a) Remember area is proportional to frequency for a histogram.

(b) Explain your method before using your calculator by giving a full expression of where the answer is coming from.

10. (a) (i) $\sin\left(2x - \dfrac{\pi}{3}\right) = \dfrac{1}{2} \;\Rightarrow\; 2x - \dfrac{\pi}{3} = \dfrac{\pi}{6}, \dfrac{5\pi}{6}, \dfrac{13\pi}{6}, \dfrac{17\pi}{6}$ **M1   A1**

$x = \dfrac{\pi}{4}, \dfrac{7\pi}{12}, \dfrac{15\pi}{12}, \dfrac{19\pi}{12}.$ **A1** (any two)   **A1** (further two)   **maximum 4 marks**

(ii) $\sec^2 x - \tan x - 3 \;\Rightarrow\; \tan^2 x - \tan x - 3 = 0$ **M1**

$(\tan x - 2)(\tan x + 1) = 0 \qquad \tan x = 2 \quad \text{or} \quad -1$ **A1**

$x = 1.107, 2.356, 4.249, 5.498.$

A1 (any two)   **A1** (further two)   **maximum 4 marks**

(b)   Sketch   **B1**

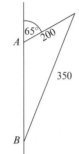

$\dfrac{\sin B}{200} = \dfrac{\sin 115°}{350}$ **M1   A1**

$\Rightarrow \;\; \sin B = 0.5179$

$\Rightarrow \;\; B = 31.19°$ **A1**

Bearing of B from $C = 211.2°$.   **M1   A1   6 marks**

TIP

(a)   (i) For $2x$ you have *4 values* in $(0, 2\pi)$ to find. (ii) Remember $\sec^2 x = 1 + \tan^2 x$.
(b)   Draw a clear diagram and then use the sine rule. Note: bearing of B from C is required.

---

11. (a) $A \equiv (-\tfrac{1}{2}, 0), \qquad B \equiv (0, 1).$ **B1   B1   2 marks**

(b) $\dfrac{dy}{dx} = 2e^{-x} - (1 + 2x)e^{-x} = e^{-x}(1 - 2x)$ **M1   A1**

$\dfrac{d^2y}{dx^2} = e^{-x}(-2) - e^{-x}(1 - 2x) = (2x - 3)e^{-x}.$ **A1   A1   4 marks**

(c) At M $x = \tfrac{1}{2}.$ $M \equiv (\tfrac{1}{2}, 1.213)$ **B1**

At M $\dfrac{d^2y}{dx^2} = (1 - 3)e^{-\frac{1}{2}} = -ve \qquad \therefore \quad$ Maximum   **M1   A1   3 marks**

(d) $\displaystyle\int (1 + 2x)e^{-x}\,dx = -(1 + 2x)e^{-x} + \int 2e^{-x}\,dx$ **M1** (direction)   **A1**

$= -(1 + 2x + 2)e^{-x} = -e^{-x}(3 + 2x)$ **A1**

Area $= \displaystyle\int_{-\frac{1}{2}}^{\frac{1}{2}} (1 + 2x)e^{-x}\,dx = [-e^{-x}(3 + 2x)]_{-\frac{1}{2}}^{\frac{1}{2}}.$ **M1   A1**

$= -4e^{-\frac{1}{2}} + 2e^{\frac{1}{2}}.$ **A1   6 marks**

TIP

(b)   Use the product rule to find $\dfrac{dy}{dx}$ and $\dfrac{d^2y}{dx^2}$.

(d)   Use integration by parts with $u = 1 + 2x$ and $\dfrac{dv}{dx} = e^{-x}$.

Solutions to Paper 4 (Pure Mathematics)

1. (a) $x + \dfrac{2}{x} = 3 + \sqrt{7} + \dfrac{2}{3 + \sqrt{7}} \dfrac{(3 - \sqrt{7})}{(3 - \sqrt{7})} = 6.$ **M1   A1   2 marks**

(b) $\left(x + \dfrac{2}{x}\right)^2 = x^2 + \dfrac{4}{x^2} + 4 \;\Rightarrow\; x^2 + \dfrac{4}{x^2} = 36 - 4 = 32.$ **M1   A1   2 marks**

TIP

Notice how multiplying by $\dfrac{3 - \sqrt{7}}{3 - \sqrt{7}}$ clears the denominator of surds.

2. (a) $1 - 3^{2x} = (1 - 3^x)(1 + 3^x)$.　**B1**　**1 mark**

(b) If in geometrical progression, then third term is

$(1 - 3^{2x})(1 + 3^x) = 1 + 3^x - 3^{2x} - 3^{3x}$.　**M1 A1**　**2 marks**

Confirms geometric progression.

(c) Next term $\Rightarrow (1 + 3^x - 3^{2x} - 3^{3x})(1 + 3^x)$　**M1**

$= 1 + 2.3^x - 2.3^{2x} - 3^{4x}$.　**A1**　**2 marks**

TIP

$(1 + 3^x)$ is the common ratio of the progression and the key to all the solution.

3. (a) $x^2 + y^2 = (9\sin^2 t + \sin^2 3t - 6\sin t \cos 3t) + (9\cos^2 t + \cos^2 3t - 6\cos t \cos 3t)$

　　　　　　　　　　　　　　　　　　　　　　　　　　　　B1 B1

$= 9 + 1 - 6(\cos t \cos 3t + \sin t \sin 3t)$

$= 10 - 6\cos 2t$.　**M1 A1**　**4 marks**

(b) Furthest from origin when $\cos 2t = -1 \Rightarrow 2t = \pi, t = \dfrac{\pi}{2}$　**M1 A1**

Distance $\sqrt{16} = 4$.　**A1**　**3 marks**

TIP

Make use of $\cos^2 A + \sin^2 A \equiv 1$ and $\cos(A - B) \equiv \cos A \cos B + \sin A \sin B$.

4. (a) Sketch　**M1**

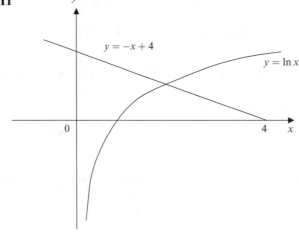

Straight line cuts graph $y = \ln x$ once

$\Rightarrow$ Only one root　**A1**　**2 marks**

(b) $f(x) = \ln x + x - 4$

$\left.\begin{array}{l} f(2.9) = -0.035 \ < 0 \\ f(3.0) = \ \ \ 0.0986 > 0 \end{array}\right\}$ continuous f　**M1**

$\Rightarrow$ root in $[2.9, 3.0]$.　**A1**　**2 marks**

(c) $f(2.95) = 0.3181 \Rightarrow$ Root between 2.95 and 2.9

$f(2.925) = -0.0017 \Rightarrow$ Root between 2.925 and 2.95　**M1**

$f(2.93) = 0.005 \Rightarrow$ Root between 2.93 and 2.925

$f(2.927) = 0.00098 \Rightarrow$ Root between 2.927 and 2.925

$f(2.926) = -0.00096 \Rightarrow$ Root between 2.926 and 2.927

$f(2.9265) = 0.0003 \Rightarrow$ Root between 2.9265 and 2.926　**A2**

$\Rightarrow$ Required root $= 2.926$. (to 3 decimal places)　**3 marks**

TIP

  (a)   The curve and this line cross where $\ln x = -x + 4$. That is $\ln x + x - 4 = 0$.
  (c)   The change of sign confirms the location of the root in $(2.9260, 2.9265)$.

5. (a)   Gradient line L is 2.

        Gradient line perpendicular to L is $-\frac{1}{2}$ **B1**

        Required equation of M $\Rightarrow$ $y + 1 = -\frac{1}{2}(x - 3)$ **M1**

        i.e. $2y + x = 1$.   **A1**   **3 marks**

    (b)   Intersection with line L $\Rightarrow$ $4x - 2y + 11 = 0$ **M1**

                    $2y + x = 1$

        $\Rightarrow$ Adding $5x = -10$

        $\Rightarrow$ $x = -2$, $y = \frac{3}{2}$ **A1   A1**

        Reflection of A in L $\Rightarrow$ $B \equiv (-7, 4)$.   **A1   A1**   **5 marks**

TIP

    Sketch the lines L and M.

6. (a)   Sketch   **B2**   (b)   Sketch   **B2**

        coordinates   **B1**   **3 marks**   coordinates   **B1**   **3 marks**

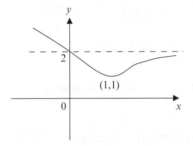

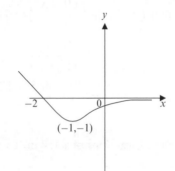

    (c)   Sketch   **B2**

        coordinates   **B1**   **3 marks**

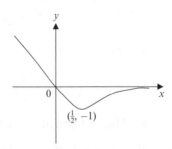

TIP

    Don't forget to show the coordinates of the minimum point in each case.

7. (a) $V = \frac{4}{3}\pi r^3$, $S = 4\pi r^2$ $\Rightarrow$ $V^2 = \dfrac{(4\pi r^2)^3}{3^2 \pi \cdot 4} = \dfrac{S^3}{36\pi}$.   **M1   A1**   **2 marks**

    (b) $2V\dfrac{dV}{dS} = \dfrac{3S^2}{36\pi}$ $\Rightarrow$ $\dfrac{dV}{dS} = \dfrac{1}{12\pi} \cdot \dfrac{(4\pi r^2)^2}{\frac{4}{3}\pi r^3}\dfrac{1}{2} = \dfrac{r}{2}$.   **M1   A1   A1   A1**   **4 marks**

(c) $\dfrac{dS}{dt} = \dfrac{dS}{dV}\cdot\dfrac{dV}{dt} = \dfrac{2}{r}\cdot 4 = \dfrac{8}{r}$ **M1 A1**

When $V = 36\pi = \dfrac{4}{3}\pi r^3 \Rightarrow r^3 = 27 \quad r = 3$ **B1**

$\Rightarrow \dfrac{dS}{dt} = \dfrac{8}{3}.$ **A1   4 marks**

TIP

Learn for a sphere that $V = \tfrac{4}{3}\pi r^3$, $A = 4\pi r^2$.

8. (a) $\dfrac{\frac{1}{45}}{15 - x} - \dfrac{\frac{1}{45}}{60 - x}.$ **B1 B1   2 marks**

(b) $\displaystyle\int \dfrac{1}{(15 - x)(60 - x)}\, dx = \int K\, dt$ **M1**

$\Rightarrow \dfrac{1}{45}[-\ln(15 - x) + \ln(60 - x)] = Kt + C$ **A1 A1**

$t = 0, x = 0 \Rightarrow C = \dfrac{1}{45}\ln 4$ **M1 A1**

When $t = \dfrac{1}{3}$ $x = 6 \Rightarrow \dfrac{1}{3}K + \dfrac{1}{45}\ln 4 = \dfrac{1}{45}\ln\left(\dfrac{54}{9}\right)$

$\Rightarrow K = \dfrac{3}{45}\ln\left(\dfrac{3}{2}\right)$ **A1**

$\Rightarrow \dfrac{1}{45}\ln\left(\dfrac{60 - x}{15 - x}\right) = \dfrac{3}{45}\ln\left(\dfrac{3}{2}\right)t + \dfrac{1}{45}\ln 4$

When $t = 1$ $\ln\left(\dfrac{60 - x}{15 - x}\right) = 3\ln\left(\dfrac{3}{2}\right) + \ln 4 = \ln\left[\left(\dfrac{3}{2}\right)^3\cdot 4\right]$ **M1**

$\Rightarrow \dfrac{(60 - x)}{(15 - x)} = \dfrac{27}{2} \Rightarrow 120 - 2x = 405 - 27x$

$\Rightarrow x = \dfrac{405 - 120}{25} = 11\tfrac{2}{5} = 11.4.$ **A1   8 marks**

TIP

The partial fractions enable you to integrate the differential equation.

9. (a) (i) Coeff. $x^4 = \dfrac{14\cdot 13\cdot 12\cdot 11}{1\cdot 2\cdot 3\cdot 4} = 1001.$ **M1 A1   2 marks**

(ii) Coeff. $x^5 = 1001 \times \dfrac{10}{5} = 2002.$ **A1**

Coeff. $x^6 = 2002 \times \dfrac{9}{6} = 3003.$ **A1**

$\Rightarrow$ Hence form an AP first term 1001 common difference 1001.   **A1   3 marks**

(b) $S_n = \dfrac{n}{2}[2a + (n - 1)d] > 1{,}001{,}000$ **M1**

$\Rightarrow \dfrac{n}{2}[2002 + 1001(n - 1)] > 1{,}001{,}000$ **A1**

$\Rightarrow 1001n^2 + 1001n - 2002000 > 0$
or $n^2 + n - 2000 > 0$ **A1**

But $\left.\begin{array}{l}44^2 + 44 = 1980\\ 45^2 + 45 = 2070\end{array}\right\} \Rightarrow n > 44$ **M1**

Number of terms required is 45.   **A1   5 marks**

10. (a) $\dfrac{dx}{dt} = -3\cos^2 t \sin t$ $\dfrac{dy}{dt} = 3\sin^2 t \cos t$ **B1**   **B1**

       $\Rightarrow \dfrac{dy}{dx} = \dfrac{dy}{dt} \cdot \dfrac{dt}{dx} = -\dfrac{\sin t}{\cos t}.$ **M1**   **A1**   **4 marks**

    (b)   Gradient of normal $= \dfrac{\cos t}{\sin t}.$ **M1**

       Equation normal $\Rightarrow y - \sin^3 t = \dfrac{\cos t}{\sin t}(x - \cos^3 t)$ **M1**

             $\Rightarrow x \cos t - y \sin t = \cos^4 t - \sin^4 t.$ **A1**   **3 marks**

    (c) $\cos^4 t - \sin^4 t = (\cos^2 t - \sin^2 t)(\cos^2 t + \sin^2 t)$ **M1**

                 $= (\cos^2 t - \sin^2 t) \cdot 1 = \cos 2t.$ **A1**   **2 marks**

    (d)   Normal $\Rightarrow x \cos t - y \sin t = \cos 2t$

       $A \Rightarrow y = 0, \; x = \dfrac{\cos 2t}{\cos t}$ **M1**   **A1**

       $B \Rightarrow x = 0, \; y = -\dfrac{\cos 2t}{\sin t}$ **A1**

       $AB^2 = \cos^2 2t \left(\dfrac{1}{\cos^2 t} + \dfrac{1}{\sin^2 t} \right) = \dfrac{4\cos^2 2t}{4\cos^2 t \sin^2 t}$ **M1**

          $= \dfrac{4\cos^2 2t}{\sin^2 2t} = 4\cot^2 2t$

       $\Rightarrow AB = 2\cot 2t.$ **A1**   **5 marks**

11. (a) $0 = 3^2 - c$ $c = 9.$ **B1**   **1 mark**

    (b) $\dfrac{dx}{dy} = -2y$, when $y = 3$ $\dfrac{dx}{dy} = -6$ **M1**   **A1**

       $\left. \begin{array}{l} \text{Eq. tangent at } A \quad y - 3 = -\frac{1}{6}x, \; 6y - 18 + x = 0 \\ \text{Eq. tangent at } B \quad y + 3 = \frac{1}{6}x, \; 6y + 18 - x = 0 \end{array} \right\}$ **M1**   **A1**

       Meet where $-36 + 2x = 0$ $x = 18, \; y = 0.$ **A1**   **5 marks**

    (c) $\displaystyle\int (9 - x)^{\frac{1}{2}}\,dx = -\tfrac{2}{3}(9 - x)^{\frac{3}{2}} \Rightarrow \int_0^9 (9 - x)^{\frac{1}{2}}\,dx = 18$ **M1**   **A1**   **A1**

       Area $APB = 3 \times 18 = 54$ **A1**

       $\Rightarrow$ Required area of $R = 54 - 36 = 18.$ **A1**   **5 marks**

    (d) $\displaystyle\int \pi y^2\,dx = \pi \int (9 - x)\,dx = \left[9x - \dfrac{x^2}{2} \right]\pi$ **M1**   **A1**

       $\Rightarrow \displaystyle\int_0^9 \pi y^2\,dx = \pi \left[81 - \dfrac{81}{2} \right] = 40\tfrac{1}{2} \cdot \pi$ **A1**

       Volume of cone $= \tfrac{1}{3}\pi r^2 h = \tfrac{1}{3}\pi \cdot 3^2 \cdot 18 = 54\pi$ **B1**

       Volume of nose cone $= 54\pi - 40\tfrac{1}{2}\pi = \tfrac{27}{2}\pi$

              $\approx 42.4\,\text{m}^2.$ **A1**   **5 marks**

Mechanics solutions and marks

Note that in each solution, the topic, or topics, being examined is/are identified (in the tips). This is a vital first step in any Mechanics solution.

Diagrams should be used wherever possible in your own solutions, showing all the information given. This is usually the vital second step.

Always make sure your final answer is given *to the degree of accuracy* asked for by the Examiner.

Solutions to Paper 5 (Mechanics)

1. Using $S = ut + \frac{1}{2}at^2$ with $S = 2000$, $t = 40$, $u = 60$ and $a = -r$, for the retardation **M1**

    $2000 = 60 \times 40 - \frac{1}{2} \times r \times 40^2$ **A1**

    $2000 = 2400 - 800r \Rightarrow r = \frac{1}{2}$ **A1**

    The uniform retardation is $\frac{1}{2}\,\mathrm{ms}^{-2}$.

    Using $v^2 = u^2 + 2as$ with $v = 0$, $u = 60$, $a = -\frac{1}{2}$ and $S = AC$

    $O = 60^\circ - 2 \times \frac{1}{2} \times AC$ **M1**

    $AC = 3600$ **A1**

    $BC = AC - AB = 3600 - 2000 = 1600.$ **A1**

    The distance between B and C is 1600 m.   **6 marks**

> **TIP**
>
> *Uniform acceleration in a line.*
> Sketch a diagram with the data included.

2. Suppose **P** has magnitude λ newtons and **Q** μ newtons.

    Unit vector in direction $4\mathbf{i} + 3\mathbf{j} = \dfrac{4\mathbf{i} + 3\mathbf{j}}{|4\mathbf{i} + 3\mathbf{j}|} = \dfrac{4\mathbf{i} + 3\mathbf{j}}{5}$ **B1**

    That is $\mathbf{P} = \lambda\left(\dfrac{4\mathbf{i} + 3\mathbf{j}}{5}\right) = \dfrac{\lambda}{5}(4\mathbf{i} + 3\mathbf{j})$ **B1**

    (similarly $\mathbf{Q} = \dfrac{\mu}{5}(-3\mathbf{i} - 4\mathbf{j})$

    Since $\mathbf{P} + \mathbf{Q} = \mathbf{R}$, we have

    $\dfrac{\lambda}{5}(4\mathbf{i} + 3\mathbf{j}) - \dfrac{\mu}{5}(3\mathbf{i} + 4\mathbf{j}) = 70\mathbf{i}$ **M1**

    The **i** components must be equal and the **j** components too

    $\left.\begin{array}{l} \frac{4}{5}\lambda - \frac{3}{5}\mu = 70 \\ \frac{3}{5}\lambda - \frac{4}{5}\mu = 0 \end{array}\right\}$ **A1**

    Solving simultaneously gives $\lambda = 200$, $\mu = 150$ **M1 A1**

    Hence $\mathbf{P} = 160\mathbf{i} + 120\mathbf{j}$, $\mathbf{Q} = -90\mathbf{i} - 120\mathbf{j}$.   **A1**   **7 marks**

> **TIP**
>
> *Forces, vectors and unit vectors.*
>
> Unit vector in direction of a is $\dfrac{a}{|a|}$.

3. Since equilibrium is limiting

$F = \mu R$ where $\mu = \frac{3}{4}$, $R = 2g$

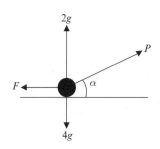

Frictional force $= \frac{3}{4} \times 2g = \frac{3}{2}g$.   **B1**

Balancing forces horizontally gives $P \cos \alpha = \frac{3}{2}g$ **M1   A1**

Balancing forces vertically gives $P \sin \alpha = 4g - 2g$ **M1   A1**

So we have $P \cos \alpha = \frac{3}{2}g$ and $P \sin \alpha = 2g$

$\left. \begin{array}{l} \text{Dividing } \tan \alpha = \dfrac{2g}{\frac{3}{2}g} = \dfrac{4}{3} \;\Rightarrow\; \alpha = 53.1° \\[3mm] \qquad\qquad P = \dfrac{2g}{\sin \alpha} = 24.5 \end{array} \right\}$ **M1   A1   A1   8 marks**

TIP

Forces acting on a particle in equilibrium.
Use a clearly labelled sketch.

4.

Before   →3   ←1
(0.1 kg)   (0.2 kg)

After   ←u   →u

(a) By conservation of linear momentum

$0.1 \times 3 - 0.2 \times 1 = 0.2 \times u - 0.1 \times u$ **M1   A1**

Solving gives $u = 1$.   **A1   3 marks**

(b) Kinetic Energy Loss $=$ K.E. before $-$ K.E. after

$= (\frac{1}{2} \times 0.1 \times 3^2 + \frac{1}{2} \times 0.2 \times 1^2 - \frac{1}{2} \times 0.1 \times 1^2 - \frac{1}{2} \times 0.2 \times 1^2) \text{J}$ **M1   A1**

$= (0.45 + 0.1 - 0.05 - 0.10) \text{J}$

$= 0.4 \,\text{J}$.   **A1   3 marks**

(c) Impulse exerted by B on $A =$ change in momentum of A

$= 0.1 \times 3 - (-0.1 \times 1) \,\text{Ns}$ **M1   A1**

$= 0.4 \,\text{Ns}$.   **A1   3 marks**

TIP

Momentum, kinetic energy, impulse
Consider the *whole system* for energy loss but only *one sphere* for impulse.
Note how the sketch helps with the signs.
(a) & (b)   Use the system in the solution.
(c)   Uses only particle A in its solution.

---

5. (a) So $\dfrac{\mathrm{d}v}{\mathrm{d}t} = 2 + 4t$ **M1**

Integrating gives $v = 2t + 2t^2 + \text{Constant}$ **A1**

At time $t = 0$, $v = 3$ so we have

$3 = 0 + 0 + \text{Constant}$ $\therefore$ Constant $= 3$ **B1**

and $v = 2t^2 + 2t + 3$

when $t = 3$, $v = 2 \times 9 + 2 \times 3 + 3 = 27$ **M1**

speed is $27 \,\text{ms}^{-1}$ when $t = 3$.   **A1   5 marks**

(b) $\dfrac{dx}{dt} = 2t^2 + 2t + 3$ **M1**

$x = \frac{2}{3}t^3 + t^2 + 3t + \text{Constant}$ **A1**

$x = 0$ when $t = 0$ so Constant $= 0$.   **B1**

Distance covered between $t = 1$ and $t = 3$ is

$[\frac{2}{3}t^3 + t^2 + 3t]_1^3 = [18 + 9 + 9 - (\frac{2}{3} + 1 + 3)]\,\text{m}$ **M1**

$= 31\frac{1}{3}\,\text{m}.$ **A1**   **5 marks**

TIP

Variable acceleration: solving differential equations.

In calculus notation $\dfrac{dv}{dt} = $ acceleration, $v = \dfrac{dx}{dt} = $ velocity.

(a) Notice how to find the constant.

(b) You need to write $v = \dfrac{dx}{dt}$ here.

6. (a) Using notation in diagram shown.

Newton II for A gives: $0.9g - T = 0.9\lambda g$ **M1**   **A1**

Newton II for B gives: $T - 0.85g = 0.85\lambda g$.   **A1**

Adding $0.05g = 1.75\lambda g$ **M1**

$\lambda = \dfrac{0.05}{1.75} = \dfrac{1}{35}.$ **A1**   **5 marks**

(b) On substituting for $\lambda \Rightarrow$ $T = 0.85g + 0.85g \times \frac{1}{35}$ **M1**

$T = 8.568 \Rightarrow$ Tension is 8.568 N.   **A1**   **2 marks**

(c) From rest A moves down a distance of $\frac{1}{2} \times 0.28 \times 4\,\text{m} = 0.56\,\text{m}$ **M1**   **A1**

B moves up same distance, so change is P.E. $= (0.9 - 0.85)0.56 \times 9.8\,\text{J}$ **M1**

$= 0.2744\,\text{J}.$ **A1**   **4 marks**

TIP

Connected particles: Newton's laws.
Use Newton II for each particle in turn.

7. Using Newton II, force acting at speed v at time t is

$800\dfrac{dv}{dt}$ **M1**

Power $= $ force $\times$ velocity $= 800v\dfrac{dv}{dt} = 40\,000$ **M1**   **A1**

Hence we have $v\dfrac{dv}{dt} = 50.$ **A1**

Separating the variables and integrating gives

$\frac{1}{2}v^2 = 50t + \text{Constant}$ **M1**   **A1**

$v = 0$ at $t = 0$ so Constant $= 0$ **A1**

Hence $v^2 = 100t$

$v = 20, t = \dfrac{400}{100} = 4.$ **M1**

Car takes 4 s to reach speed of 20 ms^{-1}.   **A1**   **9 marks**

(b)   Sketch   **B2**   **2 marks**

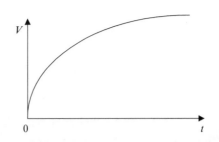

8. (a) Tabulate the work with this question.

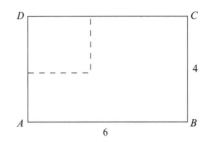

	Rectangle $ABCD$	Square	Rectangle	
C.M. from BC	3 m	5 m	$\bar{x}$	**B1**
C.M. from AB	2 m	3 m	$\bar{y}$	**B1**
Relative Mass	$24\,\text{m}^2 \equiv 6M$	$4\,\text{m}^2 \equiv M$	$20\,\text{m}^2 \equiv 5M$	**M1 A1**

Taking moments about BC we have

$18M = 5M + 5\bar{x}M \Rightarrow \bar{x} = \frac{13}{5}.$ **M1   A1**

Taking moments about AB we have

$12M = 3M + 5\bar{y}M \Rightarrow \bar{y} = \frac{9}{5}.$ **M1   A1**   **8 marks**

(b) The centre of mass G is vertically below C when hung up at C.   **B1**

Required angle is $\widehat{BCG}$, and $\tan \widehat{BCG} = \dfrac{\frac{13}{5}}{4 - \frac{9}{5}} = \dfrac{13}{11}$ **B1 M1**

Angle $BCG = 50°$. (to the nearest degree)   **A1   4 marks**

9. (a) From G_1 to G_2, the potential energy loss
$= 70g(10 - 10\cos 70°)\,\text{J}.$ **M1   A1**

Kinetic Energy gain $= \frac{1}{2} \times 70 \times v^2$ **B1**

These are equal so

$v^2 = 2g(10 - 10\cos 70°)$ **M1**

$v = 11.4\,\text{ms}^{-1}.$ (to 3 significant figures)   **A1**   **5 marks**

(b) Tension is greatest when girl is at lowest point, as shown, moving with speed $11.4\,\text{ms}^{-1}$:

acceleration towards O is $\dfrac{11.4^2}{10}$ **B1**

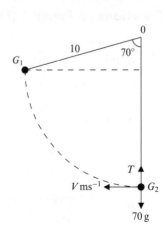

Using Newton II $\quad T - 70g = 70\left(\dfrac{11.4^2}{10}\right)$ **M1 A1**

Hence $T = 1590\,\text{N}$. (to 3 significant figures) **M1 A1** **5 marks**

(c) Modelling assumptions are: rope is **light** and **inextensible** **B1 B1**

girl is modelled as a particle. **B1** **3 marks**

10. (a) (i) Initial vertical component of velocity $= u\sin 33°$ **B1**

Using $s = ut + \tfrac{1}{2}at^2$ vertically with $a = -g$ and $s = 0$ gives $0 = ut\sin 33° - \tfrac{1}{2}gt^2$, where t is time from A to B, **M1**

that is $t = \dfrac{2u\sin 33°}{g}$ **A1**

As the horizontal component of velocity is constant and is $u\cos 33°$ we have from A to B

$AB = (u\cos 33)\left(\dfrac{2u\cos 33}{g}\right)$ and $AB = 26\,\text{m}$, **M1**

$u^2 = \dfrac{26g}{2\cos 33° \sin 33°} \Rightarrow u = 16.7\,(\text{ms}^{-1})$. **M1 A1** **6 marks**

(ii) Using $v^2 = u^2 + 2as$, we obtain greatest height h from

$O = 16.7^2 \sin^2 \alpha - 2gh$ **M1**

$h = \dfrac{16.7^2 \sin^2 33}{2g} = 4.22\,\text{m}$. **M1 A1** **3 marks**

(iii) Time from A to B is $\dfrac{2 \times 16.7\sin 33°}{g}$ **M1**

$= 1.9\,\text{s}$. **A1** **2 marks**

(b) The ball has been modelled as a particle. **B1**

It has been assumed that air resistance can be neglected. **B1** **2 marks**

Solutions to Paper 6 (Mechanics)

1. $\dfrac{140}{\sin(90° - \alpha)} = \dfrac{100}{\sin(180 - \alpha)}$

But $\sin(90° - \alpha) = \cos\alpha$, and $\sin(180 - \alpha) = \sin\alpha$ **M1**

so we have $\dfrac{140}{\cos\alpha} = \dfrac{100}{\sin\alpha} \Rightarrow \tan\alpha = \dfrac{10}{14}$, $\alpha = 35.5°$ **A1 A1**

$\dfrac{P}{\sin(360° - 270° + 2\alpha)} = \dfrac{100}{\sin\alpha}$ (using Lami's theorem) **M1**

$P = \dfrac{100\sin(90° + 2\alpha)}{\sin\alpha} = 55.8$. **M1 A1** **6 marks**

TIP

Forces at a point: Lami's theorem
Note how to use Lami's theorem.

2.

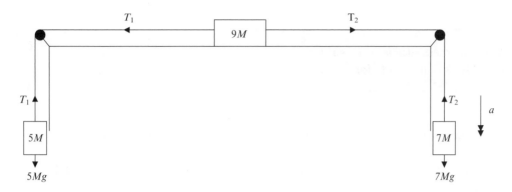

Suppose acceleration of each is $a\,\mathrm{ms}^{-2}$ and that the tensions are T_1, T_2 newtons, as shown above.

For $5M$ body, $\quad T_1 - 5Mg = 5Ma$ $\hspace{4cm}$ (1) $\quad$ **M1** $\quad$ **A1**

$\qquad 9M$ body, $\quad T_2 - T_1 = 9Ma$ $\hspace{4cm}$ (2) $\hspace{2.3cm}$ **A1**

$\qquad 7M$ body, $\quad 7Mg - T_2 = 7Ma$ $\hspace{4cm}$ (3) $\hspace{2.3cm}$ **A1**

Equations (1), (2) and (3) are the result of applying Newton II in turn to each body.

Adding (1), (2) and (3) gives

$2Mg = 21Ma$ so $a = \dfrac{2}{21}g$ $\quad$ **M1** $\quad$ **A1**

From (2), $T_2 - T_1 = \dfrac{18}{21}Mg = \dfrac{6}{7}Mg$ $\quad$ **A1**

So acceleration is $\dfrac{2}{21}g$ and its difference in tensions is $\dfrac{6}{7}Mg$. $\quad$ **7 marks**

TIP

Motion of connected particles: Newton's laws.
Copy the diagram and add your own symbols for Tension and Acceleration. Apply Newton II
to each particle.

3. (a) (i) Suppose car (C) and motorcycle (M/C) cover x metres in t seconds, then

For C, $x = 17t$ (as there is no acceleration) $\quad$ **B1**

For M/C, $x = 10t + \frac{1}{2} \times 0.8 \times t^2$ $\quad$ **M1**

Solving simultaneously we have $7t = 0.4t^2$

and $t = \dfrac{7}{0.4}\,\mathrm{s} = 17.5$ seconds at overtaking point. $\quad$ **M1**

Distance $AB = 297.5$ metres. $\quad$ **A1** $\quad$ **4 marks**

(ii) Speed of M/C at $B = (10 + 0.8 \times 17.5)\,\mathrm{ms}^{-1} = 24\,\mathrm{ms}^{-1}$. $\quad$ **M1** $\quad$ **A1** $\quad$ **2 marks**

(b) Sketch   **B1** **B1**   **2 marks**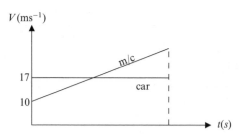

TIP

Uniform acceleration in a straight line.
(a) Use $s = ut + \frac{1}{2}at^2$ for each.

---

4. (a) Acceleration $= \dfrac{1.4}{0.2}$ ms$^{-1} = 7$ ms^{-1} (Using $F = ma$)   **M1** **A1**

Speed acquired in $3\,\text{s} = 7 \times 3$ ms$^{-1} = 21$ ms^{-1} (Using $v = u + at$)   **B1**

Distance covered in $3\,\text{s} = \frac{1}{2} \times 7 \times 9$ m $= 31.5$ m (Using $s = ut + \frac{1}{2}at^2$).   **B1**   **4 marks**

(b) From 21 ms^{-1}, P comes to rest in 35 m, under uniform retardation r ms^{-2}.

Using $v^2 = u^2 + 2as \Rightarrow O = 21^2 - 2 \times r \times 35$ **M1**

$$r = 6.3.\quad \textbf{A1}$$

Magnitude of retarding force $= (0.2)(6.3)$ newtons (from Force $=$ mass $\times$ retardation)

Retarding force $= 1.26$ N.   **B1**

Time to stop is given by $O = 21 - 6.3t$ (by using $v = u + at$)

i.e. time to stop $= 3\frac{1}{3}$ s.   **B1**   **4 marks**

TIP

Newton's laws of motion.
Take care with signs in the equations.

---

5. (a) Horizontal force at A is μR because equilibrium is limiting.   **B1**

Force on rod at B is horizontal because wall is smooth.   **B1**

Taking moments about A,

$S \times 8\sin 32° = 15g \times 4\cos 32°$ **M1** **A1**

$S = 117.6$ N   **A1**   **5 marks**

(b) Forces $\uparrow =$ Forces $\downarrow \Rightarrow R = 15g$ **M1**

Forces $\rightarrow =$ Forces $\leftarrow \Rightarrow \mu R = S$ **M1**

Hence $\mu = \dfrac{117.6}{15g} = 0.8.$ **M1** **A1**   **4 marks**

(c) In the solution, the actual length of rod is NOT required.   **B1**   **1 mark**

TIP

Body in limiting equilibrium, including friction.
Draw a sketch including all the forces acting on the rod.

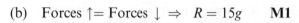

6. (a) Time to highest point $= \dfrac{20 \sin 37°}{g} = 1.228\,\text{s}$ **M1 A1**

Height of highest point above the sea $= 42 + \dfrac{20^2 \sin^2 37}{2g}$ metres. **M1 A1**

$= 49.39$ metres. **A1 5 marks**

(b) Time taken to fall 49.39 m from rest is given by $49.39 = \frac{1}{2} \times 9.8 \times t^2$ **M1 A1**

$t = \sqrt{\dfrac{49.39}{4.9}} = 3.175\,\text{s}.$ **A1**

Time taken by projectile to reach sea

$= (1.228 + 3.175)\,\text{s} = 4.40\,\text{s}$ (to 3 significant figures). **A1 4 marks**

(c) Horizontal distance of B from A

$= 20 \cos 37° \times (4.40)$ metres **M1**

$= 70.3\,\text{m}.$ **A1 2 marks**

TIP

Free motion of projectiles under gravity.
Consider the motion in two stages, A to H then H to B.

---

7. (a) Extension in $BP = 1$ metre **B1**

Hooke's law

$T = \dfrac{70 \times 1}{1.5}\,\text{N} = \dfrac{140}{3}\,\text{N}.$ **M1 A1 3 marks**

(b) $BC = 1.5\,\text{m}$, $\cos\alpha = \frac{3}{5}$, $\sin\alpha = \frac{4}{5}$ **M1 A1**

Resolve vertically $T\cos\alpha = mg$ **M1**

Hence $mg = $ weight of particle $= \dfrac{140}{3} \times \dfrac{3}{5}\,\text{N} = 28\,\text{N}.$ **A1 4 marks**

(c) *Note*: Acceleration in circular motion is $\dfrac{V^2}{2}$ here.

Newton II horizontally $T\sin\alpha = m \cdot \dfrac{V^2}{2}$ **M1 A1**

Giving $V^2 = \dfrac{2T\sin\alpha}{m} = \dfrac{2g\sin\alpha}{\cos\alpha} = 2g\left(\dfrac{4}{3}\right)$ **M1**

$V = 5.11\,\text{ms}^{-1}.$ **A1 4 marks**

(Figure: right triangle with vertex B at top, angle α; $2.5\,\text{m}$ along hypotenuse PB; P at lower left with mg acting downward and tension T along PB; base $PC = 2\,\text{m}$ with C at lower right.)

TIP

Elastic string; Hooke's law; circular motion.
Note weight is mg.

8.

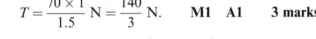
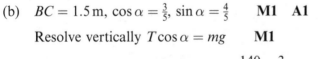

Before → 6 ms^{-1} → 2 ms^{-1}

X (0.3 kg) Y (0.4 kg)

After → V_1 ms^{-1} → V_2 ms^{-1}

(a) Impulse on $X =$ change in its momentum

$0.3(6 - V_1) = 1.2 \ \Rightarrow\ V_1 = 2.$ **M1 A1 2 marks**

(b) Conservation of linear momentum on the system

$0.3 \times 6 + 0.4 \times 2 = 0.3 \times 2 + 0.4 \times V_2$ **M1** **A1**

$V_2 = 5$.   **A1**

Newton's experimental law for collisions:

e(rel. speed of approach) = (rel. speed of separation)

$e(6 - 2) = 5 - 2 \Rightarrow e = \dfrac{3}{4}$.   **M1** **A1**   **5 marks**

(c) Loss in kinetic energy

$= [\frac{1}{2} \times 0.3 \times 6^2 + \frac{1}{2} \times 0.4 \times 2^2 - (\frac{1}{2} \times 0.3 \times 2^2 + \frac{1}{2} \times 0.4 \times 5^2)] \, \text{J}$ **M1** **A1**

$= 0.6 \, \text{J}$.   **A1**   **3 marks**

(d) No loss of K.E. if particles are perfectly elastic.   **B1**

In this case, $e = 1$.   **B1**   **2 marks**

TIP

Conservation of momentum, Newton's experimental law, kinetic energy.
(a) Draw a sketch.
(b) Note how to use Newton's experimental law and *signs* correctly.
(c) Consider whole system for loss in K.E.

---

9. (a) Period $= \dfrac{2\pi}{\omega} = 2.6$ so $\omega = \dfrac{\pi}{1.3}$ and $a = 2.8 \, \text{m}$.   **B1**

Greatest speed occurs at centre of motion and greatest acceleration occurs at ends of the motion.   **B1**

Greatest speed $= \omega a = \dfrac{\pi}{1.3} \times 2.8 \, \text{ms}^{-1} = 6.77 \, \text{ms}^{-1}$.   **M1** **A1**

Greatest acceleration $= \omega^2 a = \left(\dfrac{\pi}{1.3}\right)^2 \times 2.8 \, \text{ms}^{-1} = 16.35 \, \text{ms}^{-2}$.

    M1 **A1**   **6 marks**

(b) Using the formula $V^2 = \omega^2(a^2 - x^2)$ with $V = 3$, and a and ω as above gives

$9 = \left(\dfrac{\pi}{1.3}\right)^2 (2.8^2 - x^2)$ **M1** **A1**

$x = 2.51$.   **A1**

When speed is 3, platform is 2.51 m from the centre of its motion.   **3 marks**

(c) The body will tend to leave the platform after the halfway stage of its rise.

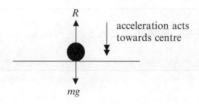

The acceleration at distance x from centre is $\left(\dfrac{\pi}{1.3}\right)^2 x$

So $mg - R = m\left(\dfrac{\pi}{1.3}\right)^2 x$ (Newton II)   **M1** **A1**

$R = 0$ at instant body leaves platform

So $x = g\left(\dfrac{1.3}{\pi}\right)^2 = 1.68\,\text{m}.$ **M1**

Distance $h = 2.8 + 1.68\,\text{metres}$

$= 4.48\,\text{metres from lowest point.}$ **A1**   **4 marks**

TIP

Simple Harmonic Motion.
(a) Use the formulae acc. $= |\omega^2 x|$, $\text{vel}^2 = \omega^2(a^2 - x^2)$.
(c) $R = 0$ is the condition needed when body leaves the platform.

10. (a) Using $\mathbf{F} = m\mathbf{a}$ at time t, in the usual notation, we have

$2\dfrac{\mathrm{d}^2\mathbf{r}}{\mathrm{d}t^2} = 3\mathbf{i} + 12t^2\mathbf{k}$ **M1**

Integrating with respect to t gives

$2\dfrac{\mathrm{d}\mathbf{r}}{\mathrm{d}t} = 3t\mathbf{i} + 4t^3\mathbf{k} + \mathbf{C}_1$, where $\mathbf{C}_1$ is a vector constant   **M1**   **A1**

When $t = 0$, $\dfrac{\mathrm{d}\mathbf{r}}{\mathrm{d}t}$ (or $\mathbf{v}$) $= 4\mathbf{i} - 2\mathbf{j}$

so $\mathbf{C}_1 = 8\mathbf{i} - 4\mathbf{j}$ **B1**

and $2\dfrac{\mathrm{d}\mathbf{r}}{\mathrm{d}t} = (3t + 8)\mathbf{i} - 4\mathbf{j} + 4t^3\mathbf{k}$ **A1**

Momentum of body at time $t = m\mathbf{V} = 2\mathbf{V}$

$t = 2$, Momentum $= (14\mathbf{i} - 4\mathbf{j} + 32\mathbf{k})\,\text{Ns}.$ **M1**   **A1**   **7 marks**

(b) Kinetic Energy $= \frac{1}{2}m\mathbf{V}^2$

At $t = 2$. K.E. $= \frac{1}{2} \times 2 \times |7\mathbf{i} - 2\mathbf{j} + 16\mathbf{k}|^2\,\text{J}$ **M1**

$= 309\,\text{J}.$ **A1**   **2 marks**

(c) Integrating the velocity equation gives

$2\mathbf{r} = (\frac{3}{2}t^2 + 8t)\mathbf{i} - 4t\mathbf{j} + t^4\mathbf{k} + \mathbf{C}_2,$ **M1**   **A1**

where $\mathbf{C}_2$ is a vector constant.

At $t = 0$, $\mathbf{r} = \mathbf{i} + \mathbf{j} + \mathbf{k}$ $\Rightarrow$ $\mathbf{C}_2 = 2\mathbf{i} + 2\mathbf{j} + 2\mathbf{k}$ **A1**

and $\mathbf{r} = \frac{1}{2}[(\frac{3}{2}t^2 + 8t + 2)\mathbf{i} + (2 - 4t)\mathbf{j} + (t^4 + 2)\mathbf{k}]$ **M1**

At $t = 2$, position vector of the body is

$(12\mathbf{i} - 3\mathbf{j} + 9\mathbf{k})\,\text{metres}.$ **A1**   **5 marks**

TIP

Vectors in 3D (but ignoring gravity).
Keep your algebraic expressions tidy at each stage or you could get lost.

Solution to Paper 7 (Mechanics)

Note: acceleration $= \dfrac{\mathrm{d}v}{\mathrm{d}t} = \dfrac{\mathrm{d}v}{\mathrm{d}x} \cdot \dfrac{\mathrm{d}x}{\mathrm{d}t} = v\dfrac{\mathrm{d}v}{\mathrm{d}x},$ since $v = \dfrac{\mathrm{d}x}{\mathrm{d}t}$

1. Using Newton II $mv\dfrac{\mathrm{d}v}{\mathrm{d}x} = -mcx^2$ **B1**

Separate variables $\displaystyle\int v\,\mathrm{d}v = \int -cx^2\,\mathrm{d}x$

$\dfrac{v^2}{2} = -c\dfrac{x^3}{3} + K.$ **M1**   **A1**

At time $t = 0$, $x = a$, $v = 0$, so $K = \frac{1}{3}ca^3$ **M1**

and $\dfrac{v^2}{2} = \frac{1}{3}c(a^3 - x^3)$.   **A1**

At $x = 0$, $v^2 = \frac{2}{3}ca^3 \Rightarrow v = \sqrt{\frac{2}{3}ca^3}$.   **A1**   **6 marks**

> **TIP**
>
> Variable acceleration in a line, using $v\,\dfrac{dv}{dx}$ form.
>
> Note − sign in differential equation.

2. (a) The weight component of A down the plane is $10\,mg\,(0.6)\,$N.   **B1**

     Let T newtons be tension in the string.

     Equation of motion for A is $T - 6\,mg = 10\,ma$.   **M1**   **A1**

     Equation of motion for B is $8\,mg - T = 8\,ma$.   **A1**

     Solving gives $2\,mg = 18\,ma \Rightarrow a = \frac{1}{9}g$.   **A1**   **5 marks**

   (b) $T = 8\,mg - \dfrac{8}{9}\,mg \Rightarrow T = \dfrac{64}{9}\,mg$.   **M1**   **A1**   **2 marks**

> **TIP**
>
> Connected particles: Newton's laws.
> Use the diagram and mark in the forces acting.

3.

Let N be point where string first becomes slack, as shown in the diagram.

Extension at $B = \frac{1}{2}L$ **B1**

Energy in string at $B = \dfrac{1}{2} \times \dfrac{12\,mg\left(\frac{L}{2}\right)^2}{L} = \dfrac{3}{2}\,mg\,L$ **M2**   **A1**

Kinetic energy at $N = \frac{1}{2}mV^2$ **M1**

Energy conservation so $\frac{1}{2}mV^2 = \frac{3}{2}\,mg\,L$ **M1**

$V = \sqrt{3gL}$.   **A1**   **7 marks**

> **TIP**
>
> Energy in an elastic string.
>
> Use the formula $E = \dfrac{1}{2}\dfrac{\lambda x^2}{\ell}$ for the stretched elastic string.

4. (a)

Resolving vertically $R\cos\alpha = 1000\,g$.   **M1**   **A1**

Applying Newton II horizontally $R\sin\alpha = 1000\,\dfrac{21^2}{100}$ **B1**   **M1**   **A1**

Solving gives $\dfrac{\sin \alpha}{\cos \alpha} = \tan \alpha = \dfrac{21^2}{100\,g}$ **M1**

$\alpha = 24.2°.$ **A1**   **7 marks**

(b) In the solution the car is modelled as a particle.   **B1**

The car could be modelled as a larger body with four contact points and the centre of mass above the ground.   **B1**   **B1**   **3 marks**

> **TIP**
>
> *Circular motion.*
> *Car on a banked circular track.*
> *In circular motion at constant speed v, acceleration* $= \dfrac{v^2}{r}$, *directed towards the centre of the circle, radius r.*

5. (a) Water raised per second $= \pi \times 0.1^2 \times 6 \times 1000\,\text{kg}$ **M1**

$= 60\pi\,\text{kg}.$ **A1**

Gain in potential energy each second $= 60\pi \times 9.8 \times 20\,\text{J}.$ **B1**

Gain in kinetic energy each second $= \frac{1}{2} \times 60\pi \times 6^2\,\text{J}.$ **B1**

Total work done each second by the pump $= 40\,340\,\text{J}.$ (to 4 significant figures)

   M1   **A1**   **6 marks**

(b) Impulse of force on wall $=$ change in momentum of water.

Change in momentum in 1 second $= 60\pi \times 6\,\text{Ns}.$ **M2**

Steady force being applied by water $= 360\pi\,\text{N}$ **M1**

$= 1131\,\text{N}.$ **A1**   **4 marks**

> **TIP**
>
> *Work, power and energy: impulse.*
> *Consider the motion for 1 second.*
> *In this final stage we are using the formula* $Ft = m(v - u)$ *with* $t = 1$.

6. (a) On the surface of the moon, let acceleration due to gravity be $g'\,\text{ms}^{-2}$ and consider a particle of mass $m\,\text{kg}$ on the surface.   **M1**

Force $= mg' = \dfrac{GMm}{R^2}$, where M is the mass of moon

$g' = \dfrac{6.67 \times 10^{-11} \times 7.36 \times 10^{22}}{(1.74 \times 10^6)^2}$ **M1**   **A1**

$= 1.62.$ **A1**   **4 marks**

(b) The time to fall is found using $s = ut + \frac{1}{2}at^2$

$100 = \frac{1}{2} \times 1.62 \times t^2$ **M1**   **A1**

$t = 11.1\,\text{s}.$ **A1**   **3 marks**

(c) Acceleration due to gravity on the surfaces of the earth and the moon are in ratio $9.8 : 1.62.$ **M1**

Weight of rock on earth's surface $= \dfrac{124 \times 9.8}{1.62}\text{N}$ **M1**

$= 750\,\text{N}.$ (to 2 significant figures)   **A1**   **3 marks**

> **TIP**
>
> *Newton's law of universal gravitation.*

7. (a) Time to reach post is found by considering
        horizontal direction.

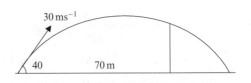

$$\text{Time} = \frac{70}{30 \cos 40°} \text{ seconds} \quad \textbf{M1} \quad \textbf{A1}$$

$$= 3.046\,\text{s} \quad \textbf{A1}$$

The height of post can now be found using $s = ut + \frac{1}{2}at^2$ vertically.

$$\text{Height} = (30 \sin 40°)(3.046) - \frac{1}{2} \times 9.8 \times (3.046)^2 \text{ metres} \quad \textbf{M1} \quad \textbf{A1}$$

$$= 13.3\,\text{m.} \quad \textbf{A1} \qquad \textbf{6 marks}$$

    (b) **Velocity** means that we need to find **magnitude** and **direction**.

        Vertical component of velocity at top of post $= 30 \sin 40° - 9.8(3.046)\,\text{ms}^{-1}$ **M1**

        $$= -10.75\,\text{ms}^{-1} \ (- \text{ implies down}) \quad \textbf{A1}$$

        Horizontal component $= 30 \cos 40° = 22.98\,\text{ms}^{-1}$ **B1**

        Magnitude of velocity $= \sqrt{22.98^2 + 10.57^2} = 25.3\,\text{ms}^{-1}$ **M1**   **A1**

        Direction of velocity $= \arctan \dfrac{10.57}{22.98} = 24.7°$ to horizontal downwards.   **A1**   **6 marks**

TIP

Projectile motion.
Use a clear diagram when forming equations. Notice that **velocity** is a vector quantity.

8. (a) Forces acting on rod are shown in diagram.

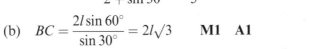

        Friction force is μR.   **B1**

        Resolving horizontally $T \cos 30° = \mu R$.   **B1**

        Vertically $Mg + T \sin 30° = R$.   **M1**   **A1**

        Moments about A

        $Mgl \cos 60° = T2l \sin 30°$ **M1**

        which simplifies to $T = \frac{1}{2}Mg$ **A1**

        Hence $\mu = \dfrac{\cos 30°}{2 + \sin 30°} = \dfrac{\sqrt{3}}{5}$.   **M1**   **A1**   **8 marks**

    (b) $BC = \dfrac{2l \sin 60°}{\sin 30°} = 2l\sqrt{3}$ **M1**   **A1**

        Hooke's law $T = \frac{1}{2}Mg = \dfrac{\lambda l\sqrt{3}}{l\sqrt{3}} \Rightarrow \lambda = \frac{1}{2}Mg$.   **M1**   **A1**

        The modulus of elasticity is $\frac{1}{2}Mg$.   **4 marks**

TIP

Limiting friction, body in equilibrium.
(a) Copy the diagram and put in all the forces on the rod.
(b) Note that Hooke's law is needed for the final part.

9. (a) (i) Suppose that P is at height S_2 metres and S_3 metres at $2s$ and $3s$ after leaving
            ground with speed $u\,\text{ms}^{-1}$. Using $s = ut + \frac{1}{2}at^2$,

            $$S_2 = 2u - \frac{1}{2} \times 9.8 \times 4 \quad \textbf{M1} \quad \textbf{A1}$$

            $$S_3 = 3u - \frac{1}{2} \times 9.8 \times 9 \quad \textbf{A1}$$

            $$S_3 - S_2 = 45 \ \Rightarrow \ 45 = u - \frac{5}{2}g \ \Rightarrow \ u = 69.5. \quad \textbf{M1} \quad \textbf{A1} \qquad \textbf{5 marks}$$

(ii)   Greatest height $= \dfrac{69.5^2}{2g}$ m.   **M1   A1**

      $= 246.4$ m.   **A1**   **3 marks**

(iii)   We need to find *twice* the time taken to fall $(246.4 - 78.4)$ metres from rest.   **M1**

Time above 78.4 metres $\Rightarrow$ time $= 2 \times \sqrt{\dfrac{168}{\frac{1}{2} \times 9.8}}$ seconds   **M1   A1**

      $= 11.7$ s.   **A1**   **4 marks**

(b)   The modelling assumption made is that air resistance can be neglected.   **B1**   **1 mark**

> **TIP**
>
> *Vertical motion under gravity.*
> (a)   The key to the solution is to start at the ground each time.
> (c)   Here it's best to start from the top.

10. (a)   (i) $\mathbf{r} = (t - 2\cos t)\mathbf{i} + (2\sin t)\mathbf{j}$

Velocity at time $t = \mathbf{v} = \dfrac{d\mathbf{r}}{dt}$ **M1**

$\mathbf{v} = \dfrac{d\mathbf{r}}{dt} = (1 + 2\sin t)\mathbf{i} + (2\cos t)\mathbf{j}$ **M1   A1**

$|\mathbf{v}^2| = 1 + 4\sin t + 4\sin^2 t + 4\cos^2 t$ **M1**

Using $\cos^2 t + \sin^2 t = 1$, $|\mathbf{v}|^2 = 5 + 4\sin t$ **A1**

$5 + 4\sin t$ is least when $\sin t = -1$ **M1**

Then, $t = \dfrac{3\pi}{2}$.   **A1**   **7 marks**

(ii)   When $t = \dfrac{3\pi}{2}$, $\overrightarrow{OQ} = \dfrac{3\pi}{2}\mathbf{i} - 2\mathbf{j}$.   **M1   A1**   **2 marks**

(b)   Acceleration at time $t = \mathbf{a} = \dfrac{d\mathbf{v}}{dt}$ **M1**

So $\mathbf{a} = \dfrac{d\mathbf{v}}{dt} = (2\cos t)\mathbf{i} - (2\sin t)\mathbf{j}$ **A1**

$|\mathbf{a}|^2 = 4\cos^2 t + 4\sin^2 t = 4$.   **M1**

Since $|\mathbf{a}|$ is constant, the force acting on Q is constant in magnitude.   **A1**   **4 marks**

> **TIP**
>
> *Vectors: motion in a plane.*
>
> Remember $\dfrac{d\mathbf{r}}{dt} =$ velocity, $\dfrac{d^2\mathbf{r}}{dt^2} = \dfrac{d\mathbf{v}}{dt} =$ acceleration.

Solutions to Paper 8 (Mechanics)

1.

Forces balance vertically $R_A + R_B = 111\,g$.   **B1**

Moments about B $9.5R_A = 31\,g \times 4.5 + 80\,g \times 5.5$ **M1   A1**

$R_A = 61\,g$.   **A1**

Force at A is 597.8 N and force at $B = 490$ N.   **A1**   **5 marks**

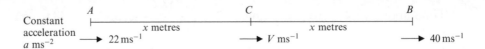

2.

Using notation in the diagram with $v^2 = u^2 + 2as$

AC: $v^2 = 22^2 + 2ax$ **M1** **A1**

AB: $40^2 = 22^2 + 4ax$ **A1**

eliminating the ax terms   **M1**

$2v^2 = 40^2 + 22^2$ **M1**

$v = 32.3.$ **A1**

The speed at C is $32.3 \, \text{ms}^{-1}$.   **6 marks**

3. (a) Weight component of lorry down the plane is

   $10\,000\,g \times 0.15 \, \text{N}$ **M1**

   Total force = weight component + resistance

   $= 24\,560 \, \text{N}$ **A1**

   Work done by engine$= 24\,560 \times 12 \, \text{watts}$ **M1**

   $= 295 \, \text{kW}$. (to the nearest kW)   **A1**   **4 marks**

   (b) Using Newton II on trailer

   $T - 5450 = 6500 \times 0.13$ **M1** **A1**

   $T = 6295.$ **A1**

   Tension in tow-bar is 6295 N.   **3 marks**

4. (a) (i) Friction force $= 0.65R$.   **B1**

           Forces up and down

           $R = 3Mg$.   **B1**

           Forces left and right

           $S = 0.65R$.   **B1**

           Hence $S = 1.95Mg$.   **B1**   **4 marks**

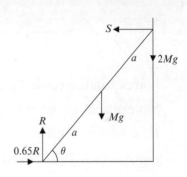

(ii) Taking moments about the foot of the ladder

$$Mga\cos\theta + 4Mga\cos\theta = 2aS\sin\theta \qquad \textbf{M1} \quad \textbf{A1}$$

$$\tan\theta = \frac{5}{3.9} \;\Rightarrow\; \theta = 52°.\text{ (to the nearest degree)} \qquad \textbf{M1} \quad \textbf{A1} \qquad \textbf{4 marks}$$

(b) The ladder is modelled as a uniform straight rod.   **B1**   **1 mark**

> **TIP**
>
> *Limiting equilibrium: friction.*
> Draw a sketch and show all forces, modelling the ladder as a uniform rod of mass M.

5.

Before $\longrightarrow u$ at rest   Collision of A and B.

       $(m)\,A$ $(m)\,B$

After $V_A \longrightarrow$ $V_B \longrightarrow$

Using notation in the diagram.

Conservation of momentum $Mu = MV_A + MV_B$ **M1**

Newton's collision law $V_B - V_A = eu$ **M1**

Solving to obtain $V_A = \dfrac{(1-e)}{2}u,\ V_B = \dfrac{(1+e)}{2}u$ **M1**   **A1**   **A1**

Before $\dfrac{u}{2}(1+e) \longrightarrow$ at rest   Collision of B and C

       $(m)\,B$ $(m)\,C$

After $V'_B \longrightarrow$ $V_C \longrightarrow$

Conservation of momentum $\Rightarrow V'_B + V_C = \dfrac{u}{2}(1+e)$ **M1**

Newton's collision law $\qquad\qquad V_C - V'_B = \dfrac{Eu}{2}(1+e)$ **M1**

Solving to obtain $V'_B = \dfrac{1}{2}(1-E)\dfrac{u}{2}(1+e)$ **A1**

A and B will not collide again if

$V_A < V'_B$ **M1**

$\dfrac{1-e}{2} < \dfrac{1}{4}(1+e)(1-E)$ **A1**

$\dfrac{2(1-e)}{1+e} < 1 - E \;\Rightarrow\; E < \dfrac{1+e-2+2e}{1+e}$ **A1**

$\Rightarrow\; E < \dfrac{3e-1}{e+1}$, as required   **11 marks**

> **TIP**
>
> *Collisions: conservation of momentum: Newton's collision law.*
> Draw a clear sketch to show your notation at each collision.
> Note you don't need to find V_C.

6. Using notation in diagram, $\tan \theta = \frac{3}{4}$

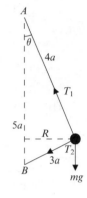

$\sin \theta = \frac{3}{5}$, $\cos \theta = \frac{4}{5}$ **M1**   **A1**

$R = 4a \sin \theta = \frac{12a}{5}$.   **B1**

Resolving vertically forces balance

$T_1 \cos \theta - T_2 \sin \theta = mg$ **M1**

$4T_1 - 3T_2 = 5mg$ (1)   **A1**

Newton II horizontally, (acc $= R\omega^2$ towards centre)

$T_1 \sin \theta + T_2 \cos \theta = mR\omega^2$ **M1**

$3T_1 + 4T_2 = 12ma\omega^2$ (2)   **A1**

Solving (1) and (2) for T_2 gives

$T_2 = \frac{3m}{25}(16a\omega^2 - 5g)$.   **M1**   **A1**

Strings are both taut if $T_2 \geqslant 0$ **M1**

That is, $\omega^2 \geqslant \frac{5g}{16a}$.   **A1**   **11 marks**

TIP

Circular motion.
Note that the tensions are different in the strings. Add all forces to *your own* diagram.

7. (a) Take a strip parallel to x-axis at distance y
from O of thickness δy.

Movement of strip about x-axis is $2xy\,\delta y$.   **M1**

Sum of moments $= \displaystyle\int_0^a 2y\sqrt{a^2 - y^2}\,\mathrm{d}y$ **A1**

$= \left[-\frac{2}{3}(a^2 - y^2)^{\frac{3}{2}} \right]_0^a$ **A1**

$= \frac{2}{3}a^3$.   **A1**

Moment of whole area about x-axis $= \dfrac{\pi a^2}{2} \times \bar{y}$ and these are equal, so

$\dfrac{\pi a^2}{2}\,\bar{y} = \dfrac{2}{3}a^3$ **M1**

$\bar{y} = \dfrac{4a}{3\pi}$, as required   **A1**   **6 marks**

(b) Distance of centre of mass of semicircle from bounding diameter $= \dfrac{80}{3\pi}$ cm.   **B1**

Relative masses of semicircle and rectangle are 200π and $40b$, respectively.   **B1**   **B1**

Moments about bounding diameter of these two parts are equal if centre of mass of
whole lamina is on bounding diameter.   **M1**

$$40b \times \frac{b}{2} = 200\pi \times \frac{80}{3\pi} \quad \textbf{M1}$$

$b = 16.33.$ **A1   6 marks**

8. (a) (i) Frictional force $= 0.2R$ down plane   **B1**

$R = 2g \cos 30°.$ **B1**

Along plane $P = 0.2R + 2g \sin 30°$ **M1**

$\qquad\qquad = 0.2 \times 2g \cos 30° + 2g \sin 30°$ **A1**

$\qquad\qquad = 13.19.$ **A1**   **5 marks**

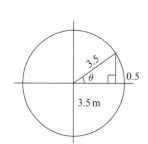

(ii) Frictional force $= 0.2R$ up the plane   **B1**

$P = 2g \sin 30° - 0.2g \cos 30°$ **M1**

$\qquad = 6.41.$ **A1**   **3 marks**

(b) Resultant force down the plane is

$(2g \sin 30° - 0.4g \cos 30°)\,\text{N}$

Acceleration $= g \sin 30° - 0.2g \cos 30°\,\text{ms}^{-2}$ **M1**

$\qquad\qquad\quad = 3.20\,\text{ms}^{-2}.$ **A1**

Using $v^2 = u^2 + 2as$ with $u = 0$

$\qquad v^2 = 2 \times 3.20 \times 1.2$ **M1**

Speed $= 2.77\,\text{ms}^{-1}.$ **A1**   **4 marks**

9. (a) **Student A**

Water rises at $\dfrac{7}{6\frac{1}{3}}$ metres per hour $= 1.105\,\text{mh}^{-1}.$ **M1   A1**

Water needs to rise 4 m, so the boat can enter at 3.619 hours after low tide, that is, at 1537.   **M1   A1**   **4 marks**

(b) **Student B**

Using S.H.M. model has $\mathbf{a} = \mathbf{3.5}$ and $\dfrac{2\pi}{\omega} = 12\frac{2}{3}$ **B1**

so $\omega = \dfrac{\pi}{6\frac{1}{3}}.$ **B1**

Water needs to rise 0.5 m above the centre of its motion.

Angle turned through   **M1**

$= 90° + 8.21° = 98.21°.$ **A1**

Time to rise $= \dfrac{98.21}{180} \times 6\frac{1}{3}$ hours   **M1**

$\qquad\qquad = 3.456$ hours.   **A1**

Earliest time for entry is 1528.   **A1**   **7 marks**

(c) Tidal rise and fall is approximated well by S.H.M and Student A's estimate is reasonable in this instance. In other cases it could be dangerous, if it were to give an entry time before it was safe. **B2** **2 marks**

10. (a) In falling $2L$, Potential Energy loss $= 2mgL$. **B1**

String is stretched to extension L so energy in string $= \dfrac{1}{2} \lambda \dfrac{L^2}{L}$, where λ is the modulus of elasticity of the string. **B1**

These are equal, so $2mgL = \dfrac{1}{2} \lambda \dfrac{L^2}{L}$ **M1**

$\lambda = 4mg$. **A1**

At the lowest point, applying Hooke's law.

Tension $= \dfrac{\lambda L}{L} = 4mg$. **M1 A1** **6 marks**

(b) Greatest speed during the fall is when the particle passes through the position where it would hang at rest, the position of statical equilibrium. Suppose the extension is then e. By Hooke's law,

Tension $= \dfrac{4mge}{L}$ **M1**

But Tension $= mg$ with particle at rest **A1**

Hence $e = \frac{1}{4}L$.

Speed is greatest at depth $\frac{5}{4}L$ below O. **A1** **3 marks**

(c) Using conservation of energy at depth $\frac{5}{4}L$ with that at O, we have

$$\frac{1}{2}mv^2 + \frac{1}{2}\frac{4mg\dfrac{L^2}{16}}{L} = mg\frac{5L}{4}$$ **M1 A1 A1**

Hence $v^2 = \frac{9}{4}gL$. **M1**

Greatest speed $= \frac{3}{2}\sqrt{gL}$. **A1** **5 marks**